CAD
for Model Engineers

D.A.G. Brown

NEXUS SPECIAL INTERESTS

Nexus Special Interests Ltd.
Nexus House
Azalea Drive
Swanley
Kent BR8 8HU

First published by Nexus Special Interests Ltd., 1999

ISBN 1-85486-189-1

Typeset by Kate Williams, Abergavenny
Printed and bound in Great Britain by Biddles Ltd., Guildford & King's Lynn

Contents

Dedicated to the memory of Tom Walshaw

Foreword

If one had suggested in the mid 1980s that model engineers could tackle computer-aided design (CAD) as a matter of course in the hobby rather than at work, alarm bells would have rung in the household accounts department, let alone the extravagance of a computer in the home. But things have changed rapidly with the advent of the personal computer and its development as a machine which is now so fast and convenient that it will perform tasks thought slow or impracticable only a few years ago.

Inspiration for this book came over lunch with Tom Walshaw (alias Tubal Cain) at the International Model Show just a few months before he died. We were discussing current projects and he was showing resolve to revise his 1988 edition of *Workshop Drawing* (Nexus Special Interests, out of print) within this current series. I suggested "How about including something about CAD, Tom; that would really bring it up to date?". This suggestion did not appeal one little bit. "That is far more up your street, as you have demonstrated at these exhibitions in the past" he replied.

So I had to agree that there was scope for another book in the Workshop Practice Series, just devoted to CAD, but what had I let myself in for I started to wonder. However, I have the distinct advantage of having got into the technique at a fairly early stage, really as a bit of a personal challenge and through finding it very useful when doing some consultancy work from home soon after my retirement. I think I was one of the first to offer the editor of *Model Engineer* some of the products from my CAD system and we quickly agreed certain conventions which suited the magazine. I know that during the past few years my own technique and presentation have improved and my speed has become quite respectable.

I was asked to carry out some demonstration work at the IMS exhibitions and this brought me face to face with many of the model engineering public who demonstrated their interest and willingness to learn the technique. I have even had telephone calls from various people I have met in this connection, seeking to discuss their problems or asking intelligent questions when they were trying to choose a system. I believe I understand what is wanted in this book; it certainly is not a substitute for the software manufacturers' operating manuals covering the specific programmes on sale. Rather it is a device of encouragement to all who seek to get into CAD, and by way of examples to short-circuit some of the learning process that took me a long time to conquer proficiently. One of the problems faced by anyone writing such a book is that all the systems are unique and their individual instructions are diverse, but there is a common thread running through all of them and this is what I seek to grasp.

With the speed at which computer technology changes it could be only a short time before any book on the subject is viewed as dated. But it should prove a helpful tool in the immediate future and the sad irony is that the original catalyst, Tom Walshaw, is not with us to judge it. It is, I feel, quite correct to dedicate this book in his memory.

D.A.G. Brown
Rutland
September 1998

Introduction

Engineering drawing has always held a special place in my affection. I am certainly not an 'artist' in the sense that I have no known ability for landscapes or portraits, but I can imagine the shapes of objects and I can obey a set of instructions to get that idea down on paper. The ability to communicate with others *exactly* what is required is the point where engineering and art diverge. The artist wants to leave something to the imagination, whereas the engineer does not. Precision is the name of the game.

Reading Tubal Cain's book, *Workshop Drawing*, his skills and enthusiasm really come through. Advice on stretching out a piece of paper to let it stabilise overnight rings a familiar bell from the past, and his caution on cleanliness at all times must be closely heeded if you are working in the traditional medium. My collection of pencils of various grades with their interesting points is still a treasured possession, as is the tray of drawing pens bought not that long ago to replace the use of spring-bow compasses. Then there is the advice about what to do if the drawing gets too cluttered in the dimensioning department. Furthermore, the list of paper sizes from which to choose was so important in the days of drawing boards and tee squares.

Now let us sweep all that away with CAD. You do not need to have any of those inhibitions and although I am not advocating grubby habits, the problems arising from soft pencils and sandpaper blocks will no longer be an issue. You must put behind you much of what you have learned about drawing office practice, although not the correct conventions which are still as important as ever. Although I try to stick to these conventions, I am not seeking to repeat what has already been written about them and it is assumed that anyone reading this book already has a working knowledge of the good practice. If you should do things wrong you can always correct your mistakes: that is lesson 1 of CAD.

The first part of the book is devoted to the general philosophy of what is required and how to go about choosing the equipment you will need for the process. The best advice is to avoid the headlong rush into the most up-to-date facilities, unless you need them for other purposes. This book is not a substitute for the software maker's handbook, but

1

seeks to offer advice about the best steps to take to become proficient.

It is self-evident that learning to draw lines and figures accurately is the cornerstone of the whole process – and it may seem odd that such a statement is made – but do not take accuracy for granted. In the early days I was surprised whenever lines came out with peculiar dimensions and it took some time to discipline myself to use the mouse in the correct fashion, so that intersections were true and lines were laid down with the orthogonal discipline in place. I suppose the drawing board analogy is failing to lock an adjustable set-square or accidentally displacing a line by half a pencil's width because the point was not sharp enough.

The maker's handbook will tell you all about how to set the layer for current working, but nowhere will you find the reason for splitting layers. Here you will find advice – the product of experimentation and my getting it wrong at first.

Similarly, the power of the editing commands is enormous and I hope that the examples given will stimulate your mind to make best use of the facilities available. In many of the drawings reproduced I have dug out live examples of my own work which should bring the subject to life. If the handbook gives an example it is normally detached and 'cold', rather like Fig. 7.1 in Chapter 7. On that subject of hatching my own experience was at first painstaking, until I worked out that you must accurately define the whole boundary of a hatch and that failure to do so would produce an unacceptable effect.

It even took me a long time to tumble to the way my particular computer set-up will handle variations in line thickness, let alone length multipliers, so you will find the clues to solving these sorts of problems for your own application – hopefully a lot quicker than I did.

The production of professional-looking text and dimensioning is most rewarding and when you are used to it, it takes no longer to carry out than doing an amateurish job. But it does take a fairly long time to learn how to get the best results. While I cannot give specific advice for individual programmes, I have sought to make the trail through the procedure a general one to get your mind working in the right direction.

Hints and tips on methods that are not always conventional form a section on their own, and again with the intention that this approach will stimulate the mind of any reader embarking on the long uphill learning process.

In view of the nature of controlling the screen image by means of a mouse, the processes of projection and development are inevitably somewhat different from those involved in the traditional drawing methods, so the subject is aired in its own chapter to show the tremendous advantages of the computer.

The chapter on plotting and printing should expel a few myths and above all lead to economical working. Again some examples are given of the advantageous features of CAD, not the least of which is the concept of drawing full size and then deciding on the scale of the drawing just before it is printed. How that departs from the original wisdom which we have all received!

You should approach the subject positively, expecting some good early results and striving for continuous improvement. Do not choose a complicated general arrangement as your first project; that will only lead to frustration. One final word of advice: buy the cheapest ream (500 sheets) of A4 paper you can find and be prepared to run through it at an alarming rate. Computer printers are very wasteful if you are not careful, but a ream can be bought for well under £3.00 at current prices at business stationers' shops – that is a small price to pay for a learning process.

CHAPTER 1

The philosophy of CAD

CAD is a good slave but a bad master. Advantages over conventional drawing boards are easily demonstrated: the technology is clean compared with paper, it is neat and tidy, precise, easy to store without loss and easy to modify.

These words could be regarded as a call to arms, but it is the intention of this book to remove the mystique that surrounds the computer process. Many model engineers have expressed cynicism about the value of computer-aided design in the hobby, but there is surely something rather more sinister in this attitude, often related to a lack of understanding of computers or a fear of them born of ignorance. It is true that the computer is a good slave but a bad master, so it is the objective of this book to try to get the reader to come to terms with the beast, or to put it another way, to try to tame this relationship between master and slave.

I know from personal experience the blank wall presented by a computer screen and the difficulty there is in scaling that wall for the first time. Going back only a few years, the computer had a major impact on office life with the advent of the word processor in place of the typewriter. Just consider the successful way in which secretarial staff made the transition, usually in a matter of weeks, from the traditional methods into the electronic age. I well remember being introduced to an early word processor in the 1970s when each machine cost around £7,000. Today a state-of-the-art word processor may be bought for a few hundred pounds.

In business it was only a matter of time before that other great bastion of conservatism, the drawing office, fell before the electronic revolution. What was particularly amazing was the way in which so many draughtsmen overcame their fear of the unknown and learned their new skills, often scaling new heights of enthusiasm in the execution of a tool far more powerful than those previously mastered. But in those early days of the 1980s, computer power was expensive and relatively slow. The CAD programs required huge and costly installations on which to run and there was much talk among the big engineering companies about compatibility of systems and the way in which information could be exchanged between drawing centres and machine shops, establishing the ground rules for CAD–CAM, which minimises the intrusion of the human operator.

In the model engineer's workshop things are rather different: not only is the need for hand work normally maintained as part of the enjoyment of the hobby, but pockets are not bottomless. Furthermore, it is not generally necessary or desirable to keep up with the foremost edge of technology to maintain interest and a challenge in the hobby.

Now it so happens that around half of all British households own a personal computer. In many cases the pace is set by the younger generation who demand the latest model which is needed to run the computer games that require the operator to be under 12 years of age to operate. Luckily for the model engineer, it is even possible to use the cast-offs from the younger generation economically to run some very effective CAD programs.

Let us now consider the merits and demerits of CAD compared with traditional drawing methods. First it is clean and tidy – there are no papers to lose, no pencil marks to rub off with messy rubbers. For the perfectionist there is no ink to spill, nor pens to wash out! Personal experience made disposal of a large drawing board an absolute necessity within months of first mastering the skills; that board has never been missed to this day.

As is demonstrated in Chapter 5, CAD is infinitely flexible in making modifications. On a drawing board, there is always the frustration of having to rub out original ideas, whereas the electronic method allows for any sensible experimentation and movement that can be dreamed up in the mind of the designer. Furthermore, neat and tidy presentation comes second nature since from the out-set, a rigid discipline is established in drawing, dimensioning and labelling.

It is possible to forego accuracy by employing freehand drawing techniques on the electronic screen, but that seems to run against the best practice; indeed the accuracy of work drawn by even the most basic CAD package exceeds that which can be achieved in the workshop. Facilities are provided to test the way in which components go together and parts correctly drawn on the screen lead to less waste of metal during manufacture; just consider how many times you have made something and then found it necessary to alter it to make it fit! Much of that should be a thing of the past.

The facility for editing and alteration of dimensions is truly amazing. Besides being able to make things fit properly, enormous advantages accrue to anyone who is genuinely trying to develop anything, be it a tool, a set of vacuum brakes or the copying of a full-sized prototype; it is easy to change dimensions, angles, shapes or even to make some parts to stand out in contrast to the background. For those who are involved in the scaling down of original artefacts found in museums, the scale facility available in a computer drawing is an extremely powerful device.

Archival storage is another advantage of the computer system. A CAD program imposes a saving discipline in which it easy to store all drawings and to retrieve them at a later date. While this may not seem important in many instances, it is an invaluable benefit when it comes to making another model, or passing information on to one's friends, let alone the possibilities for publication in the model engineering press for those so inclined.

The message to be shouted loud is that CAD saves time and materials and provides a clear discipline that is conducive to good design practice. It enhances enjoyment of the hobby and even releases space in the home where the drawing board used to live!

One word of warning: learning CAD operation does not in any way diminish the importance of correct drawing-office practice. Thus, as the master of the CAD program, *you* decide whether to draw in first or third angle projection and *you* decide on the layout, the line widths and types, and the position and sizing of the dimensioning. The program's menu will keep your hand steady on the tiller since, having set up the parameters, it will keep conditions constant unless commanded to do otherwise.

The only problem which you have to overcome is to learn a new discipline; this should, however, be not only possible but enjoyable. Read the rest of this book and systematically learn an approach to the problem. Having been born before the Second World War, I have an analogue mind and think in this sort of way. The average computer 'nerd' has a different sort of mind – digital it may be suspected. Consequently, written communications become difficult to understand and computer instructions are incomprehensible to most people born before 1960. Do not despair – computer jargon will be studiously avoided in all chapters of this book.

CHAPTER 2

Computer power required

The computing power required is already present in many homes. A word about prices and bargains can however mirror the attitude taken by model engineers to other aspects within the hobby; changing technology of CAD programs and the pitfalls of 'keeping up with the Joneses' should at the same time be borne in mind. If, however you are starting from scratch I should like to give advice on how to decide on a program that is best suited for your needs.

Personal computers

One problem with writing any book on a computer-related subject is that it will soon become out of date due to rapid advances in technology. What is offered therefore is a look through the eyes of the closing years of the 20th century. Let us examine the personal computer (PC): this term was coined in the early 1980s when it first became economical and affordable to own a desktop machine capable of carrying out the sorts of tasks which had hitherto been reserved for large commercial mainframe machines. The original targets were word processors and spreadsheet methods, in which the everyday office tasks of secretarial work and repetitive calculations were taken away from typewriters and manual calculation sheets. The manufacturers settled on some standards and conventions which gave rise to the main 'black box' or central processing unit (CPU), either vertical or for desktop placing, which has been the principal item of development over the years. A standard keyboard has rather more keys than on a typewriter and plugs into the back of the CPU. The other expensive piece of kit is a colour screen which is known these days as a Super VGA screen. Again this plugs into the back of the CPU and the whole caboodle plugs into the mains and forms a highly sophisticated but very reliable unit.

Since its introduction, the PC central unit has undergone a revolution about every three or four years; originally the main 'chip' family was described as an 80–86 processor and every few years the family has developed through the digits 286, 386, 486, 586 and more recently subdivisions of this chip known as the Pentium or Super Pentium. As each generation appears, things get faster and the ability to perform tasks gets more and more powerful. Also in the CPU is a memory chip whose size is defined in megabytes, and a hard disc on which the programs are stored and much of the work is done. The only other features of the CPU worthy of mention in this discussion are a slot or disc drive for floppy discs and a connection for a printer or plotter and for a mouse.

We are talking about a massive worldwide industry of manufacture, driven from the USA and a complementary industry which supplies the software or program material necessary if a computer is to come to life. Central to the heart of the machine is a Disc Operating System or DOS which activates the millions of 'nerves' on the computer disc and creates a common language for dealing with them. Comprehending this system has been difficult over the years because it has been originated by people steeped in computer language; it has involved jargon not understood by everybody! Consequently *Microsoft* introduced a supervisory system known as *Windows* which seeks to make it easier for the average man on the street to find his way around. I am not entering into an argument about the benefits and disadvantages of the *Windows* system, but I would merely point out that if all you want to do is to operate a CAD system on a computer, then the fact that it will or will not run under *Windows* is largely irrelevant.

The computer market

When PCs first appeared, the price of a package was well in excess of £2,000. Now if you look in any of the computer hardware stores which have sprung up during the 1990s you will find a bewildering display on offer for anything over £900 for the most modern system, the price going up with the complexity. Hap-pily the most basic modern machine is more than adequate for the task which we are setting it. We do not need a compact disc drive, or ghetto-blasting equipment, nor do we require an Internet connection to enable us to carry out any CAD task. Conversely any more complicated set-up will cope even more adequately with our problems.

Just look at the customers in the average computer store and the magazines on the subject. The industry is driven by, and aimed at, the teenage market who persuade their parents that they *must* have the very latest equipment to run the latest version of *Star Wars 57* so as to keep up with the other kids in the street. From our point of view there is a useful by-product: the previous version of the computer is disposed of and has a much lower secondhand value than when it was bought. As a guide, a secondhand colour VGA screen maintains a value of about £150 in good working order, while a new keyboard only costs around £20. This means that the market value of a previous generation of computer (at present a 486) is only about £200, while even an early Pentium (ie 586) should be only £100 to £200 more (if you can get one!). In an analogous way to model engineering, there are people around whose hobby it is to repair and rebuild computer systems, bringing them up to date in the process. So, if you want a bargain, go about looking for it in the same way as you would a secondhand Myford lathe – the cost is modest!

The subject of printers and plotters is dealt with in Chapter 14, but the only other bolt-on extra which is essential is a mouse or simple pointing device. Mine has three buttons and cost £10, so we are not talking about a major investment. Some programs require a 3-button mouse and some need one with only two buttons. When you buy a mouse it comes with installation instructions but basically it takes up a tiny space on the hard disc and is ready for use every time the computer is switched on.

As I write these words I am using a five year-old program called *Generic CADD 6.0*. It is not designed to run under *Windows*, but I can gain access to it via that operating system if I so wish. When I bought it, I had looked at many of the packages that were available and selected it for ease of understanding and operation. This program has since been superseded, but progress should mean easier understanding and perhaps more facilities. In order for this book to be of use for a number of years it would be wrong to recommend a particular software package, rather to point the reader in the right direction for making an intelligent choice.

It is inevitable that when manufacturers introduce a new load of software they take advantage of the speed and capacity of the latest computers available. The result is that the latest programs may not run efficiently on an older model so, if you want to make use of older equipment, you will need to consider one of the older editions (or releases) of the software program. My own example, however, may prove useful as an illustration.

I bought a 386 computer in 1992, using it for general office work in some consultancy business in which I was involved. In its day it was quite up to date and 18 months later when I bought my CAD package it coped quite well but became rather slow for the more intricate work, especially when it came to handling the more acceptable fonts, or typefaces that were available within the program. So I had the computer up-graded to a 486DX, with 8 megabytes of memory installed. This combination serves very well indeed and I have no plans to upgrade it in the near future.

Choosing software

So how should you go about selecting first a program and then the machine on which to run it? First, note that when manufacturers are about to bring out a new release of their program they often discount the old stock by as much as 70%. Thus you can buy a real bargain which may further have the advantage of being able to run on a simpler set-up than the new release. Do not be mesmerised by a craving for 3-dimensional packages – they are extremely hungry in memory and disc space required and really have no place in model engineering work. 3-dimensional programs are fine if you are designing a large chemical plant, or even a public building – certainly machine builders use them to investigate inside their new products, to turn them around and to avoid conflicts between the different components – but just stop and think about our requirements in the hobby. Is there *really* anything that would benefit from this sort of treatment? Certainly when you are working on your own the type of drawing produced in the magazines and available from plans services is quite adequate. Surely we should leave plenty to the imagination for when the model is built!

Talk, if at all possible, to people who operate a program, especially amateurs who do not get support for it at their place of work. Avoid those programs which may have the words 'draw' or 'sketch' in their names but which are really graphic arts or artistic creation tools (it is acknowledged as an exception that *Autosketch* has many of the features of more sophisticated CAD packages). What you must have is a program which can draw and dimension to great accuracy and be capable of working in either imperial or metric units. A visit to a computer or design exhibition, such as one of those held at the NEC near Birmingham, can prove informative and you can get the staff on the manufacturers' stands to demonstrate the finer points of whatever takes your fancy. Compare the various products available and then ask the following questions:

1 Is the instruction manual written in understandable English or in the usual gobbledygook that is associated with most computer programs? I suggest that as an example you find out from the manual how to draw two lines 4.5 in. long at right angles to each other and meeting at one end.

2 What is the installed **help** programme like? All programs enable the user to call on assistance while running without deleting what is otherwise on the screen. As a guide, if you are trying to draw say a circle on the screen and call for help, the system should guide you through such an operation step by step. Just see how easy it is to understand.

3 How good is the tutorial programme for beginners? Any good programme should contain a range of tutorial material and if it is a proper engineering system, expect to find worked examples in mechanical, electrical and control engineering, as well as architecture. It is worth ploughing your way through the various sections of the tutorial, even if your interest is only in mechanical engineering, since the other disciplines often give an interesting insight into various features of the

package such as dimension definition and labelling which you will find useful in the future.

4 Is the package compatible with others? In other words, does it provide means of sending drawings out in the standard format so that they can be used elsewhere. This could prove absolutely vital if you ever want to change the package with which you work and still preserve the original drawings which you have made. The correct question to ask is "can I send out my drawings in the form of DXF files?". If the answer is "No", it is not a proper CAD package, so leave it alone.

5 What methods are used for making a drawing? How many operations are required to draw say a couple of lines such as those suggested in **1** above, and are you personally happy with this choice. To illustrate what is meant here, on some of the older packages to draw a line meant selecting this operation on a menu before pointing to the correct point on the screen, and then possibly trimming the lines to finished length, a procedure which can be very irksome.

6 What computer power is needed to run the program? Take advice here from the makers who should specify the minimum type of chip, memory and hard disc required. As you will appreciate, this operation goes hand-in-glove with selecting the computer itself and if a machine already exists, then the choice of suitable program may be somewhat limited.

Personal experience

As already stated, I operate a fairly old *Generic CADD* system to which I had applied the above criteria before buying it. I also have a rudimentary working knowledge of both *Autocad* and *Turbocad*, both of which I find more difficult to deal with and more cumbersome to operate; doubtless practice makes perfect, but as an example of where my own choice scores, when I want to draw a line from the end of another line I simply click the right-hand mouse button somewhere near it. Furthermore, all other operations in the program are instructed by a two-digit command, most of which are easy to remember as one gets familiar with the program. I can therefore operate with one hand on the mouse and the other on the keyboard, which for me is quick.

Remember, however, that things do not stand still and makers are continually seeking to improve their products. All the latest products involve pointing to little diagrams (or icons) on the screen which I personally do not find easy or logical. I suppose it is just the same as in modern motor cars, where I would far rather see a knob marked 'fog light' than a pictogram of pea soup. I wonder if I am really in the minority?

As you investigate deeper into the computer game you will doubtless be offered other pointing devices designed specifically for the CAD market, such as joysticks and matrix boxes of ever-increasing complexity and price. Do not be misled: the humble mouse is all you need and it is cheap. Other devices may be an advantage in a commercial drawing office but they have no place in our environment.

In the pages that follow I would be using a two-digit instruction in the *Generic CADD* program for almost all the actions required. In other methods it is necessary to point to an instruction or feature in different ways, but the principles are the same in all programs. It is not therefore possible to give precise advice which is universal. The advice must be generic with a small g!

CHAPTER 3

Starting the drawing process

The computer screen is really an infinite drawing board. We can indicate the origin of our drawing at say the bottom left-hand corner and its size, which then defines the limits of where we can draw. Some programs require this constraint to be put in at the outset, but I prefer to start drawing without any constraints and only to define the limits at the stage of printing, when it is possible to address the scale to be printed.

The computer will work to a millionth of an inch accuracy, far better than we need, so do not try to do things freehand, otherwise you may lose the inbuilt accuracy available.

The first step is to decide the units of working, ie imperial or metric. Look at the menu and follow your nose for the instruction on units, both displayed on the screen and those in which the data will be processed. Engineering drawings in metric units should be designated in millimetres, definitely not centimetres! For large drawings of houses etc., metres and millimetres are required and this determines the way in which you enter values of length. Similarly, imperial drawings must be defined in inches, and for larger spreads feet and inches. Any

entries made say as 1.5 or 1 ½ will be recorded as inch measurements, feet requiring an addition of a symbol, such as 3' 1 ½ ". Normally if you are working on an ordinary model drawing, there is no need to specify the units any further, since inches can be used even when the figure goes above 12.

There is one slight note of warning to sound: having set up the system in one or other of the measurement standards, you can easily switch between imperial and metric even after having done a drawing and before the dimensioning process. But there may be some tiny error in dimensions if you are working in the standard not in the basic set-up of the program. It probably would not amount to much but there seems no point in incurring errors voluntarily, so make the rule and stick to it that the system should be set up in the measurement standard that you intend to use; should you make a definite change, then return to the installation menu and instruct the computer that it should work in the other standard.

Having set the units, let us examine the constraints which are designed to help the drawing process. We can turn on a grid which appears as a pattern of dots spaced to any value we require, using a **set grid** command. It may be useful to set the grid spacing at ⅛ in. or even closer, but it may be altered at any time during the process.

The constraint of the grid may be called on or off at will and this represents the first of our **snap** features. As will be seen later, we can snap to a grid point, a line end, centre, or other feature, thereby maintaining the available accuracy.

The other important constraint to be addressed now is the orthogonal mode which can be engaged or disengaged at will. This determines that lines will normally be truly horizontal or vertical, although the angle may be set to any value from −90 to +90 degrees for drawing lines at other angles to the horizontal. Think of this facility as an adjustable tee-square, since if the X-axis is set at n degrees, then the Y-axis will be set at 90 + n degrees.

Before drawing any line, get sorted out in your own mind the discipline of layers. Here is a major departure from the traditional drawing method and it is designed to ease future modification and presentation work. The discipline which I adopt is to put all centre-lines on Layer 0, main outlines etc. on Layer 1, subassemblies on 2, dimensions on 3 and cross hatchings on 10. Depending on the complexity of a drawing I may use up to 20 different layers on a fairly arbitrary basis. However you define them, remember that you can easily change them later but that it is easier to combine layers than to split them!

Starting drawing

With the **layer current** as 0, the first line to be drawn is usually a centre-line, so select a suitable **line type** which is the traditional dash and dot line. Keep the line width to minimum and select a **line colour**, either black or white to suit your preferred screen colour. Note that whichever you select, a black line will be printed when it comes to putting it on paper. You can now draw a line, by clicking the left-hand mouse button to start it, and again to finish it, however many inches away you require. Some programs require you to refer to the coordinates of the ends of lines. In all programs the coordinates of the cursor are displayed prominently on the screen which is rather like keeping track of the movement of a draughting machine over the surface of the drawing board.

Note that at any time during the process you may **zoom** into any part of the drawing, or conversely you may make what you have drawn fill the whole screen, by means of a command such as **zoom all**. The topic of zooming is dealt with in Chapter 4.

Next change the layer to 1, the line colour to blue and the line type to continuous. The main outline can now be started, but note that you only have to draw one side of a view, the other side being mirrored at a later stage.

Let us assume that we are dealing with a piece of metal 1 in. dia and 2 in. long as the stock from which a component is to be machined: there are several ways of drawing the outline. If we have the grid constraint switched on it is easy enough to count the number of grid spaces (if all of them are actually shown on the screen) and to click the mouse button at the appropriate positions. But there are many instances where the grid is turned off and the cursor is free to roam around the screen. Let us assume that the centre-line is 4 in. long (see Fig. 3.1). Use the facility of snapping to an object, in this case the centre-line. Pointing to the

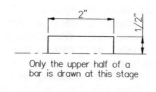

Only the upper half of a
bar is drawn at this stage

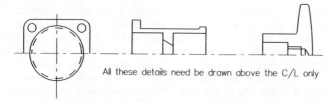

All these details need be drawn above the C/L only

Fig. 3.1 *This illustrates the need to draw only half of a symmetrical view: in the top example, half of a piece of bar may sometimes be a useful way of starting out a drawing, reminiscent of the machining process where some of the metal is removed. In the lower figure the details of a buffer are drawn above the line, but the circles are complete.*

object in question starts a line about 1 in. in from the end. Next draw the line vertically upwards for a distance of ½ in. You can instruct the computer by typing in this amount and it will register with an accuracy of 6 places of decimals; also note that it does not matter whether you call for ½ or 0.5 or .500, the response is just the same. Bearing in mind that correct engineering practice is to include the leading zero on dimensions less than 1 in., there is no point in wasting time in such fripperies while making a drawing. In some programs it is necessary to set things up for orthogonal coordinates in order that the length of a line can be called up by typing in its length.

You can now draw a horizontal line 2 in. long from the last point, followed by the final vertical line which can be snapped to the centre-line. In some programs the technique of drawing a series of adjoining lines is called polylines, but in general if you start with the correct instruction each movement of the mouse

will add another line accurately joined to the previous one.

A more realistic drawing is also shown in Fig. 3.1, namely the entire half view of a buffer which will be used as another example later. Much time will be saved by drawing only half of the view and, indeed, going as far as all these views before copying the lines shown by mirror imaging. It would be quite unproductive to draw arcs instead of the full circles which do go both sides of the centre-line. Note that the centre-lines are all on their own layer.

Now here is a pitfall: you may find it impossible to get a response to the instruction to snap to a particular object such as the centre-line because the layer response function has been turned off. This can be invaluable if you want to exclude from any operation layers other than that on which you are working. By the same token, you should become familiar with the several different levels of response built into the program when dealing with the different layers; you can turn on or off the other layers' response to editing commands, also their response to the snapping actions and finally you can hide or display any of the layers on which information has been stored. Familiarity with this facility is absolutely crucial and will save you much frustration in the early stages of learning.

You will also find that under line type there is a selection of different dots and dashes covering all the normal engineering requirements. A few of these are illustrated in Fig. 3.2. Look out for the means of changing the scale of the bits on the screen. This differs from program to program, but for example if Type 2 represents a broken line then so might type 22, 52, 72 etc., the lengths of the strokes increasing through the series. The significance of this facility is to take care of the needs of different scales of drawing: thus, for example, if you are dealing with a fiddly little component twice full size you will use the lowest number in the series, ie that with the shortest strokes, whereas if you are designing a tennis court you will use the top end of the series. It is recommended that you carry out some experiments with the various types of line to see what they really look like: they are not *necessarily* just as they appear in the instructions and when they appear in print a lot can be done by ringing the changes on the various multiplier set-

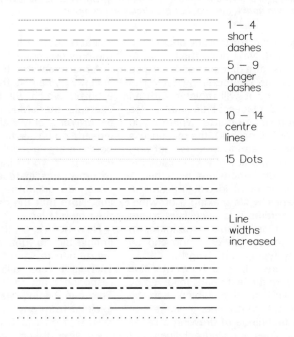

1 – 4 short dashes

5 – 9 longer dashes

10 – 14 centre lines

15 Dots

Line widths increased

Fig. 3.2 *Different line types available by choosing them from the menu provided. Note the visual effect that line enhancement has, although it does confuse the view on the screen.*

tings as well as the line thickness. Fig. 3.2 should give some clues about some of the flexibility that is available.

By clever design the program writers have contrived that however long a broken line is both ends will always be filled in, so there is no doubt about meeting points and one of the cardinal rules of drawing discontinuous lines is preserved. What happens at intersections may not always be consistent in all programs, so if it worries you that you may get a line gap coming at an intersection, then you should perform an **object break** operation on the offending line, effectively splitting it into two objects, each with its continuous ends nicely in place. The object break procedure is discussed at the end of the next chapter.

When it comes to printing the drawing you will have to instruct the program with a **size multiplier** for all lines, but this is covered in Chapter 14.

One of the advantages of the computer is the ability to draw lines of different colour on the screen. Sort out in your mind a plan of campaign and stick to it. Use the layer system to discriminate in a way that suits your requirements. One obvious way of arranging things is to use the spectral colours with appropriate layer numbers designated to them, rather like the colours allocated to electrical resistors. I much prefer to draw on a black background and I reserve white for all dimensions and lettering, besides the centre-lines.

Line enhancement

It is possible to change the line width as you proceed where, for example, the main outlines are slightly heavier than the centre-lines. The line widths are determined by a single digit from 0 to 9 or can be chosen from a chart, depend-ing upon the program, but the effectiveness of this numbering series depends on the particular printer or plotter being used. In my own case, I require Line Width 3 for the outlines, while bold lettering is done at Width 6. The subject of line enhancement is dealt with more exhaustively in Chapter 14, so for the time being take note of the following paragraph for an easy life!

If you draw using the finished widths on the screen, it will soon become illegible, so draw *everything* at minimum width and change each layer as appropriate before printing. The display will probably look awful in this form but there is a **fast redraw** facility on many programs which, if invoked, suppresses the line types and widths to the minimum value, returning legibility to the screen. Do not forget to restore the original format to the drawing before printing it!

You may be interested in the cover picture of this book, which is a photograph of my computer with a drawing on the screen. In spite of the small size of the reproduction you can clearly see many of the lines, especially those in blue and red and the bold text lines. These are all in the form in which they were emboldened before printing and the finished article is certainly very clear. On the screen, however, they are little more than a jumble of heavy strokes and should some more work on the drawing be required I would first reduce all the line thicknesses to make them legible.

Projections

Drawings in orthogonal projection pose no problem in that the lines fall naturally up and down and left and right. In isometric projection, however, there are three axes mutually at 60 degrees to each other. It is necessary to define $+30$

and −30 degrees before each stroke of the mouse in order to get the lines lying in the correct directions. This can be cumbersome and the best way around it is that described in the tutorial of the *Generic CADD* system, namely to assemble three **macros** so that a single key stroke provides the correct alignment for each of the axes. Thus (Shift F1), (Shift F2) and (Shift F3) call up the three axes vertical, +30 degrees and −30 degrees to the horizontal respectively. You should find guidance in your own tutorial to enable you to set up isometric axes easily.

Before Tom Walshaw died we were discussing the merits of trimetric projection and I should like to have included some advice on that subject in this book. However, because the scales in the different axes are not equal, I can see no way in which this kind of projection can be carried out effectively on a conventional CAD system. As you will appreciate from Chapter 11 on dimensioning, the computer remembers the lengths which have been drawn and labels them accordingly.

Most model engineering work happily goes on to orthogonal views, but there are occasions when isometric views are called for and these are quite easy to do with practice, although, as will become apparent later, there are some minor problems in displaying isometric dimensions.

Multiple lines

Some program packages allow for the setting up of multiple lines, sometimes up to 16 in number. At the low end of the scale double lines are quite often useful and all you have to do is to define the settings of the offsets from the mouse points to the left and right. Double lines are useful for such applications as drilled

ports and long holes where the lines are a fixed distance away from a centre-line. The setting up of the parameters for multiple lines has been found to be so cumbersome as to be not worth the trouble. Undoubtedly in some types of drawing they are of great value, but they are definitely not for our present application.

The art of snapping

Never try to place the end of a line by judging where it should be. Remember that the CAD system works to a very fine order of accuracy, so there is no point in sacrificing that inbuilt accuracy for no good reason. The snapping to a point has already been demonstrated and the means of achieving this varies from program to program. Other most useful constraints are also available when locating the ends of lines or positioning other items. Practise snapping to the mid point of a line or snapping to a proportional ratio and you will discover a very powerful tool: the ratio is expressed as a percentage of the distance along the line, so for example (Fig 3.3) ruler graduations can be laid down at various percentages of the way along a 1 in. scale. As you will see later, succeeding graduations will be achieved by copy editing.

Other snap commands available include the mid point of a circle or arc, a perpendicular to another line or even a curve and a tangent to a circle or arc.

It is also possible to snap a line parallel to another line at a certain distance from it, a function which may be designated as an **offset**. You may, however, find that there is a queer convention about which side of the original line the new one comes. Should you land up drawing the new line on the wrong side of the original one, change the sign of the parallel distance of separation.

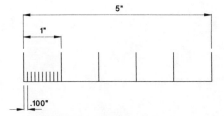

Fig 3.3 *In this simple ruler, one way of starting the 1 in. line is by choosing to snap 20% of the way along the base line to start the mark; by the same token the 1/10 in. mark can be started by snapping 2% of the way along the line.*

Tracking

Let us assume that we want to start a line not at the end of another one, but say ½ in. above it and ¾ in. away from its end.

On some programs you can use the tracking facility and track those two distances one step at a time, before commanding the computer to draw 'for real'. By these means accuracy is maintained. Tracking is a very powerful tool and can also be used in other circumstances such as during the placing of dimensions or even measuring distances. If your program does not provide a tracking facility, you may have to lay down a line in the wrong position and then drag it into the correct position as an alternative to using the coordinate system.

You should now have mastered the drawing of lines of various types, colours, widths and layers to fit together accurately on the screen. Make sure you are proficient with the ways outlined in your program before going on to the next stage.

21

CHAPTER 4

Figures and shapes: trimming and extending

If you feel confident about the method of laying down lines anywhere and at any angle, now is the time to master the drawing of other figures. You will find circles and arcs designated in the menu of your program. In general these require definition by either 2 or 3 points. A 2-point circle requires definition of its centre, again to the accuracy as before, which is then followed by the radius required. These can be indicated either by coordinates or by snapping to points already defined. A simple arc requires definition of centre and both ends. A 3-point circle or arc relies on the property that 3 points in a plane are joined by an unique circle (or circular arc), so pointing to 3 points is good enough.

Ellipses are easy to draw in CAD. The exact format varies quite a lot with the program, but the general principle is there: define the ends of the major axis, using the methods which you would to draw a line and then the prompt appears on the screen to define the length of *half* of the minor axis. If it is necessary to place the axis at an odd angle to the horizontal, you may find it simpler to draw the figure at the normal angle and then to rotate it. Some programs have an added facility of defining an ellipse as either one complete figure or as a 'constructed ellipse'. This latter configuration defines several different sections of the circumference each with its line ends, which can make future editing of the shape simpler. In all cases, however, it is possible to chop the figure about after drawing it, as will be explained below under trimming and breaking.

The facility of drawing polygons is always provided in any CAD package, but in my experience it is of very little use in engineering drawing. For example, if you want a hexagon for the end view of a nut, you may find that getting the right size and alignment requires more trouble than it is worth. It may be far better to construct one of the sides and then to do a radial copying operation as described in Chapter 6.

While on the subject of convenience, perhaps you will remember the delightful drawing office instrument the French curve. I well remember the suppressed titter that my own university lecturer on the subject raised when he suggested that we should each have one. The parallel terminology in CAD is a

Bezier curve. This facility is most useful when you want to show a flourish, say where a web on a casting runs out and there is little point in going through an elaborate procedure with bits of an ellipse and all the editing that involves. In short a Bezier curve is a way of drawing a professional-looking freehand curve, defining it by means of at least 3 points. Do study the way of finishing the end of the curve: if your mouse makes a false move there is the possibility of giving rise to an unwanted squiggle at the end of an otherwise satisfactory line.

Filleting and chamfering

All programs handle the task of filleting and chamfering in a way that demonstrates great advantages over the traditional drawing procedure. You need to set up the radius of a fillet required and then to point to the two lines which you wish to join by means of a fillet. The great power of the fillet instruction is that it will carry out the procedure irrespective of whether the two lines were originally joined or even overlapped – no dirty pencil marks are left! Points to note are that if the fillet radius is greater than, or equal to, the length of one of the lines attempted, the procedure may fail and if you are trying to fillet into the middle of a line, then the rest of it may disappear, no matter how long it was. As long as you recognise this shortcoming, you can always fill in by drawing another line in place of the length which was removed. By mastering the commands for filleting you will see how much quicker it is than trying to draw arcs as one would have done on the drawing board. The same remarks apply to chamfering, with the exception that it is necessary to fix the dimensions of both arms of the chamfer.

Trimming and extending

These two commands are often interchangeable and they are very useful during the design process. A line can be trimmed back to its intersection with another object with absolute precision, or it can be extended for future working. One obvious instance is where the centre-line has not been drawn quite long enough. Just extend it and all the dots and dashes will alter to fit the rhythm of the drawing. A centre-line should always be slightly longer than its component and this is perhaps one of the few occasions when ultimate precision is not needed.

This sort of procedure illustrates the desirability of making use of different levels; if we wish to trim a line back to another one and there is risk of confusion with the intersection with another type of line, merely turn off the editing facility relating to the object not required and the trimming target will not be missed. It is necessary to understand the 'object and target' convention which is required in your particular program; for instance in *Generic CADD* you have to point first to the object to be trimmed and then to the line back to which the operation is to take place. In *Autocad* this procedure is reversed. Whichever you master there is a period of frustration while you get used to it.

Another problem which I have noticed in some circumstances, especially when the screen is cluttered and you are trying to trim a small item, is that the operation may fail, no matter how well you think you have pointed to the objects. In these circumstances zoom into the area of operations so that it fills the screen – it is amazing what a change of magnification will do.

Breaking an object

Let us for example imagine that we have drawn several items which fit together alongside each other, making use of the same centre-line as a drawing reference. We now want to separate the items in the final version of the drawing, without losing the centre-line on either of them. Turn on the editing facility relating to the centre-line layer only and invoke the **object break** command. You should be able to operate on just that line and make a small break in it, so that the two parts will move independently. This is another powerful tool of CAD. Another good example is where you want to chew a segment out of a circle or an ellipse: instruct it to break the object and try snapping back to an intersection required to complete the editing job. You may have to finish off by trimming the loose ends of the original object as a secondary operation.

Quite frequently when you are trimming or performing other editing tasks, part of a line near the scene of operations may disappear. It may just be that the screen dots are shared between the two objects, so that when one is rubbed out it would appear that the other has also been removed. Try the **redraw** command and the desired component should be restored.

Zooming

The nominal size of the common VDU screen is only 14 in., whereas we will often be working with large drawings and frequently require to carry out small operations in one part of the view. The technique of zooming allows us to examine a very small piece of the work so that it can fill the whole screen. Indeed in some editing operations it is essential to be able to pick out a detail very closely. In all programs the zoom facility is easy to use and you can normally select a certain view by name, or even call for an exact magnification value on the screen. You can return to a named view easily. You should also look out for an allied command, **pan**, which allows you to alter the centre of the view without changing the zoom setting.

CHAPTER 5

Editing drawings

I suppose that all the modification work carried out on a drawing could loosely be classed as editing. As in the old drawing-board practice additions can be made, and in the case of the modern system the joins become invisible! But there is a regime of modification work where electronics scores without question over the traditional system. The rule for modifications is generally if you can dream of a modification which you would like to make, then it is possible quite easily with CAD. The first rule is before you start a modification make sure that the drawing is saved in its original form, so that if you get into a mess with it you can always abort it and go back to where you were.

Moving

Become familiar with the way in which your program handles the **move** command. Basically, you identify the area which you want to move – this can be any size of part containing anything from discreet lines to dimensions and text. Next choose a reference point and then indicate the new position to which you want the item to move. It should be pointed out that the reference points do

not necessarily have to be within the perimeter of the items being moved but, more to the point, you should consider the reference points that may be relevant anywhere on the drawing. As an example Fig. 5.1 shows a non-return valve in which it is desirable to check the lift of the ball. This item rises into a centre-drilled hole (60° taper). To illustrate the point the relevant bits were copied and scaled up 2.5 times below the main view, at the left illustration. In the right copy, the ball has been chosen by means of a crossing through the circle and its fill. The datum point was taken by tracking from the centre upwards at 30° to the point A. The new location of the reference point was selected by tracking upwards vertically from A to a touch point B. The two loci of these points are the two fine lines shown in the left view. The amount of movement of the ball can now be measured.

The ability to move anything on a drawing is so valuable that one of its chief attributes is to arrange the drawing layout in a neat and tidy fashion without undue cramping or blank spaces on the sheet. How often have you done a fine piece of work on a drawing board, only

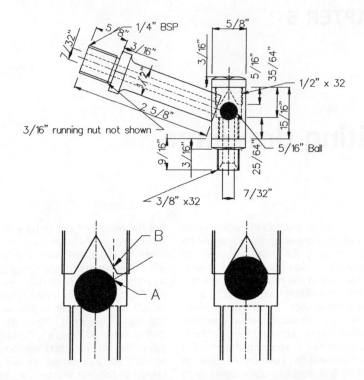

Fig 5.1 *Non-return valve with the essential bits copied and magnified below. The reference point A on the ball is moved to the new position B, touching the tapered surface. The vertical lift can now be measured.*

to discover during the dimensioning stage that there is not enough room in one area to avoid overcrowding? Therefore in a well thought-out pencil drawing there is plenty of room left around every part so that modifications and dimensioning can take place easily. Even so there is many an example of a problem before the final job is ready for printing.

Using CAD you do not have to be particularly careful about laying out the components even in the order in which they will finish up. Bearing in mind what has already been said about starting with a centre-line on its own layer, make this line longer than you might in the first instance think; it can easily be shortened or even lengthened further. The simple example in Fig. 5.1 shows how the moving command sorts out the drawing layout without making a mess. Remember the use of layers to assist you in this exercise: if the item to be moved is on one layer only, you can invoke the command to ignore all other layers and to edit only on the layer in current operation. If, as is more likely, more than one layer is present in the item to be moved,

28

then you can exercise one of two other options. The first is to identify the objects to be moved by means of windows in such a way that centre-lines and other fixed objects are not included in the move. The second option is to turn off, or hide, any layers that you do not want to be affected by the move. Make sure that you turn the layers back on when you have finished! As an example from Fig. 5.1, the movement was measured in the original drawing before construction without making the illustrative copies. The layer containing the dimensions was hidden so that its parts would not be moved.

Whoops!

In moving, as in any other stage of drawing you will soon discover that the electronic version of the rubber is the **whoops** (or oops) command. In getting to know this device, make sure that you also master the converse, otherwise called **unwhoops!** You can undo the previous several commands in the order in which they were made and then restore them if you change your mind. Do not forget, though, that the action of saving the drawing possibly cancels the ability to undo any previous commands.

From this you will soon realise that if you do not like say a new position of a component, you have several options to put matters straight without any lasting detriment.

Now if you happen to be working with a system whose memory is fairly well loaded with data, a great many editing operations may cause you to run out of space and the screen presentation may become very slow. You should find in the program menu a procedure to unload redundant information and then to repack the live data within the memory. At some

time you may find this problem arises especially when working with more than one complicated font and perhaps a number of hatching operations. Of course the long term solution is to make sure that you have enough memory on board the computer to avoid this kind of problem.

Rotation

The command to rotate can be applied to any entity in just the same way as that to move, but in rotating any object it is necessary to define an axis of rotation. The way of defining the axis and the amount of rotation desired varies slightly between programs, but the principle is the same. If dimensions already drawn are involved in a rotation, watch out what happens to them: you may get an unwanted effect of alignment, or even figures displayed upside down!

Two different applications of the rotate command are now discussed; in the first example (Fig. 5.2) a locomotive regulator is drawn out with the different components each on its own layer. The valve disc first uncovers part of one of the two small ports and then two larger ones as the handle is rotated. The rotate command makes easy work of checking the movement between stops of the regulator handle, to confirm that the large ports are just uncovered when the valve is opened fully. I know it is possible to calculate the events which are described, but it is surely easier to do the thing graphically, avoiding problems arising from such things as misinterpreting the angular distance between the cheeks of the stops.

In the second example (Fig. 5.3) a tool is drawn out in the conventional projection of elevation and plan. However, in order to emphasise the attitude taken up

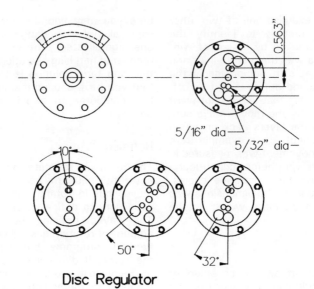

Disc Regulator

Fig. 5.2 *A locomotive regulator drawn on several layers. In the upper right view the first of the small ports is just opening, because one of the ⁵⁄₃₂ in. dia holes has been drilled 10 degrees out of alignment with the others. In the lower right view this is repeated. All the holes of the disc are put on their own layer, so that the assembly can be rotated in the middle view by another 18 degrees clockwise to show the fully closed position. Rotation of the original view by 32 degrees anti-clockwise opens the valve fully. This analysis allowed the design to be chosen with a further 10 degrees of coverage so that the valve has a full movement of 60 degrees, allowed for on the back-head stop. The regulator thus has 10 degrees of dead movement, 18 degrees of 'first valve' and 32 degrees when the main valve opens. The design has proved itself.*

by the tool in service, the plan view is rotated by 18 degrees about its central axis. It is true that the view could quite easily be drawn at the angle required and that dimensioning such an oblique view does not really present any problem, nevertheless the traditional way of drawing on X–Y axes is easier and in the case in point it was possible to determine the exact degree of rotation required graphically. Now try doing that sort of operation on a drawing board without a rubber!

Stretching and shrinking

In most programs it is possible to stretch part of a drawing, shrinking being a mathematical variation of stretching, negative sign applied! This procedure is subtly different from moving since it allows only part of a view to be moved while the bulk of it is anchored firm. In constructing the command to stretch, caution is needed when dealing with certain objects such as circles, arcs and ellipses, but if more than one attempt is needed to get perfection, not much has been lost.

30

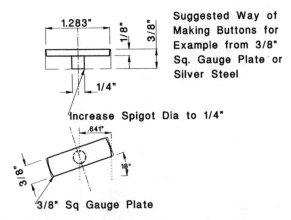

Suggested Way of
Making Buttons for
Example from 3/8"
Sq. Gauge Plate or
Silver Steel

Increase Spigot Dia to 1/4"

3/8" Sq Gauge Plate

Fig. 5.3 *Traditional projected views of a simple form tool: on the second line the plan view has been rotated so that the corner is an exact distance from the centre-line of the tool. Note the dotted construction lines in place which would normally be erased before finishing the drawing.*

There must be many instances when you wish "if only I had left another ⅛ in. on the length". The electronic way of doing things really makes life simple and, as will be seen, modifications made after the dimensioning process do not give rise to problems.

Two actual examples from my own archives illustrate the power of the method. In the first (Fig. 5.4) a small brass block is extended quite simply to improve clearances after two tapped holes came too near to the edge of the metal. In the second example (Fig. 5.5), taken from my design for safety water gauges, it became apparent after drawing them out that the design could advantageously be made shorter, thereby reducing overhang and material required and consequently improving the aesthetics of the fittings. It will be noted that the stretch operation in this case was carried out simultaneously on two dissimilar fittings (top and bottom) and that dimensions were preserved during the stretching (or shrinking) process.

Moving views farther apart along a centre-line has already been mentioned in a previous section of this chapter. By employing a **stretch** command in place of **move**, the end of a centre-line (Fig. 5.6) is still maintained at its original overhang beyond the end of the part after the stretching operation. Stretching and shrinking operations are not confined to the ends of views and items can be moved around inside finished views with great dexterity.

Exploding

You should be aware of another device which is simple to invoke, that of exploding. It will be mentioned again when it comes to dimensioning angles and that is about the only use which I have so far found for it within my particular program; different programs may retain the integrity of different entities on the screen in different ways. So, some components may stay as single items and certainly lines of text and

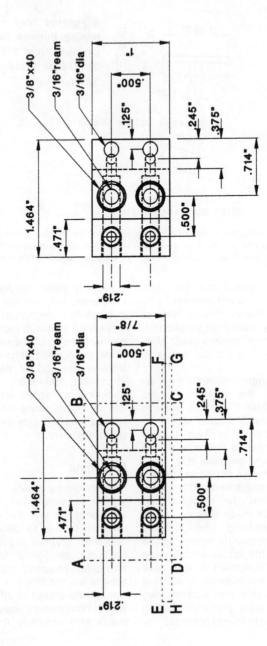

Fig. 5.4 A cylinder for a mechanical lubricator. The left-hand view was deemed to be too tight for comfort after drawing in the two tapped holes, so the top and bottom edges were stretched by ¹⁄₁₆ in. each. The whole area affected was defined by the rectangular window ABCD, while the smaller window EFGH surrounded the actual items to be stretched. Note how the dimensions kept in step.

32

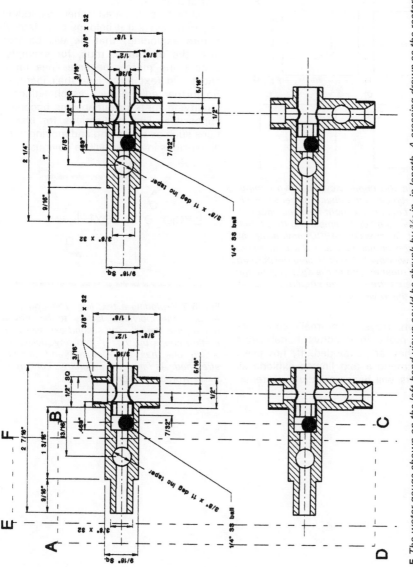

Fig. 5.5 The water gauge shown on the left-hand views could be shrunk by ³⁄₁₆ in. in length. A crossing drawn as the rectangle ABCD picked up all the lines to the left of the vertical column; these include all the parts affected by a stretching operation. The other rectangle EFGH was a window, so that all the parts totally within it were those to be stretched. The command to move all those points by ³⁄₁₆ in. to the right will be seen to have shortened the drilled passage just to the left of the ball. Note how the dimensions have changed automatically. The cross-hatching had to be reinstated separately.

33

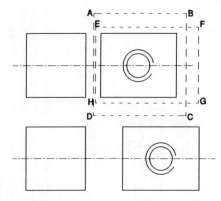

Fig. 5.6 *In the upper view the two components are too close together. The centre-line is only just beyond the right-hand component, so the move is made by employing the stretch command, a crossing ABCD embracing all parts of the component and the centre-line, while the window EFGH enclosing the parts to be moved must extend to the right beyond the end of the centre-line. The stretched result is shown in the lower view.*

dimension arrays will normally be impossible to move in unconventional ways unless they are exploded. If, however, you command a text line to explode all the letters will become individual items,

each of which can be moved around as illustrated in Fig. 5.7.

Caution is required when exploding any item, since if it belongs to a 'family' before exploding, that tie will be lost after the operation; thus, for example, dimensions merely become lines on a sheet and text fonts lose their identity. So further editing such as changing or modifying fonts or dimensions becomes impossible. The implications for operations such as stretching and moving with dimensions involved will be obvious.

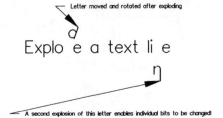

Fig. 5.7 *Exploding a text line. This operation enables the individual letters to be moved around like the 'd'. The second explosion operation chops up the 'n' into tiny pieces, of which one has been erased and another stretched. As far as the program is concerned these words no longer exist.*

34

CHAPTER 6

Editing – the power of copying

This is where the power of the computer and its ability to save time comes into its own.

The first function to consider is the **mirror image**. The principle is the same in all programs, although there are variations in the way of carrying out the command. As we saw when laying down the first few strokes in Fig. 3.1, there is only the need to draw one half of a component. By invoking the **mirror image** command, you will be asked to define what there is to copy. In common with all the other editing commands, you have a choice of several different entities to pick, anything from a single object to a whole drawing. Most are self-explanatory, but the difference between a **window** and a **crossing** is worth noting. In a window everything is picked that is within the rectangular extremities of the window drawn by the cursor; thus if a long line hangs out further than the edge of the window it will not be picked by the editing command. On the other hand a crossing picks up all items that are enclosed, or even touched, by the rectangular window that is drawn. This is a method which is selective of the items which can be affected by the operation. Consider our old friend the basic piece of bar which we have already drawn 2 in. long. I have drilled a cross hole in it, and tapped it. In selecting the items to be mirrored about the centreline, we obviously do not want to deal with the circle or arc, since to do so would lay one circle over another and even obscure the break in the arc. Illustrated in Fig. 6.1 are two ways of picking up objects which we require, one using a

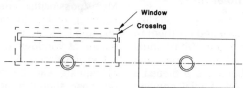

Fig. 6.1 *The left view is that of the upper half of a bar, with a tapped hole on the centre-line. The instruction to draw a mirror image is made by means of either a window or a crossing, as shown in dashes. The centre-line is used as the line of symmetry about which the reflection takes place.*

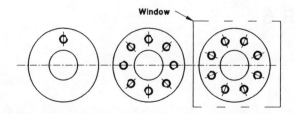

Fig. 6.2 *On the first view the tapped hole is drawn on the correct PCD on the vertical centre-line. In the second view a circular array is called for, covering 360° and containing 8 items. The third view tidies up the drawing in correct engineering practice by putting the holes 'off centres'. The command to carry out this operation tells the computer to rotate the window shown by 22.5 degrees.*

window and the other a crossing. Some circumstances lend themselves to the use of one or the other of these devices. Remember that you can turn off or even hide layers that you do not want affected by the operation.

In this simple example there is no advantage between either a window or a crossing, yet notice that the window does *not* embrace the screw thread for reasons mentioned above.

You will appreciate that the technique of drawing half of a view for copying actually creates definable points on the centre-line; for example in this component the vertical lines are actually broken in the middle. This can be of great benefit on many occasions since it enables work to be performed making use of these end points.

The radial copy or polar array

It is quite feasible to draw tiny details like 10 BA threads in full size and for them to be still legible when printed. What would become a chore if we had to repeat the operations actually becomes a pleasure to repeat electronically. Radial copying requires you to define the objects to be copied and then the point of symmetry. This might be an intersection of centre-

lines and therefore on another layer. Here is an example of where the layer in question must be turned on. You will be asked for the number of degrees for consideration (ie 360° for a complete circle) and the number of items in the span. If you want 8 items in the span as in Fig. 6.2, remember that it includes the original one being copied. You may also have to take into account the sign of rotation, ie + probably denotes anti-clockwise. A psychological pitfall comes where you are wanting to make one copy say −90 degrees from the original item. The temptation is to call for one copy in the circle and then to wonder what has gone wrong when no copy appears! It is necessary of course to count the original item in the total number.

General copying

Many possibilities arise with the tool of **copying**, or forming an array. Items are identified as in the above section by means of windows or crossings and the offset position is asked for. Any number of repeats can be requested and the response should be immediate. See example Fig. 6.3.

An obvious application of the copying facility is when assembling a general

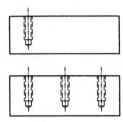

Fig. 6.3 *Having gone to great pains to draw a correct screw thread, including its pilot hole (complete with 118° end), it is a simple matter to make extra copies at the required spacing. That was a tedious business by pencil.*

arrangement from details or vice versa. I use the following procedure. From a general arrangement identify the items to be copied with the usual window. Make the copy somewhere convenient on the edge of the drawing and check that you have all the data that you require. If some are missing either repeat or have another bite at the cherry, until you are satisfied. You can then edit out any unwanted bits of the view, change the layer of the new view if desired and then move it to a convenient area of the drawing. Dimensioning can then be carried out on the copy, rather than the general arrangement. By these means the accuracy is maintained beyond question and the lining up and fit of things is discernible from the original view.

A good example of the power of this method is a drawing of a locomotive tender which was made from the original Doncaster prints. A small section of this drawing is shown in Fig. 6.4. The drawing process started with the frames and running gear and bit by bit other details were added, as the information on the prints was studied and as a full-sized version was measured. Over the months the drawing became extremely complicated,

but the CAD system never lost track of the dimensions. Everything has in fact been kept on the one sheet, although individual components have been printed for manufacture.

A simple component, a spring suspension bracket, is taken as the example, copied and developed in one corner of the drawing. As a matter of fact several months went by between the cutting and drilling of the frame steel and the making of such components as the suspension brackets in question (16 off). All fitted perfectly on assembly without any measurement of the frame holes, all drilling being done to the coordinates generated by the CAD drawing. The copying procedure used was generally in line with that already outlined and you will appreciate that on a complicated drawing it would be very easy to 'lose' items, or waste a lot of time searching for them. Consequently the use of layers, allied with colours (16 available on my screen) is another way of avoiding having to rely on the human memory! The suspension gear on the drawing in question is on Layer 6 and is bright green in colour.

I should like to give another example from my live files to illustrate how you can make life so much easier and cut down on errors. One of my abiding interests is small steam injectors and I recently decided to have a go at making the smallest size practicable, with a No 80 hole in the delivery cone. I wanted to adapt the design drawn in *Model Engineer* in 1943 by Keiller to conform with the outline pattern which I had adopted as standard, so I committed Keiller's dimensions to the screen and did the general assembly to his configuration, the cones being held on Layer 2. One by one it was a simple matter to copy each cone towards the right and I quickly had the scheme often drawn in

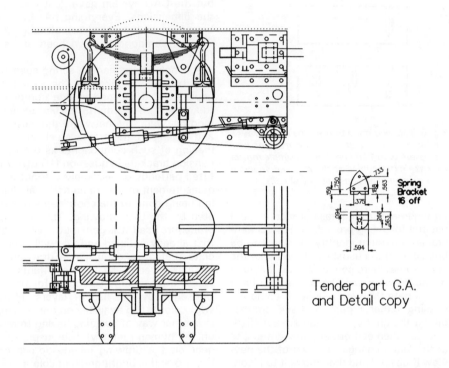

Spring
Bracket
16 off

Tender part G.A.
and Detail copy

Fig. 6.4 *Part of the drawing of a Gresley tender, showing the area around one wheel set. The small suspension bracket has been copied and developed elsewhere on the sheet, using the rules described for layers and colour. The fit on the plan view is also checked to make sure that the hole is in the correct position for the spring hanger.*

the pages of the magazine when an injector is being described. The view in Fig. 6.5 is repeated down the page to illustrate the stages in editing, but you can imagine the cones in the general arrangement being copied to the right, making use of the fact that they are on their own layer.

I have sometimes been caught out by a view such as the combining cone which contains a number of fiddly dimensions. Just consider the machining process: the

large end of the taper points towards the tailstock and it is from this end that all the critical dimensions develop. So why not draw the thing the correct way round for machining and avoid a bit of mental contortion while at the lathe? It is a simple matter to rotate the view of the combining cone about any point on the centre-line, so that it keeps itself in line with the rest of the components. For future reference observe what happens to the dimensions if you are diligent!

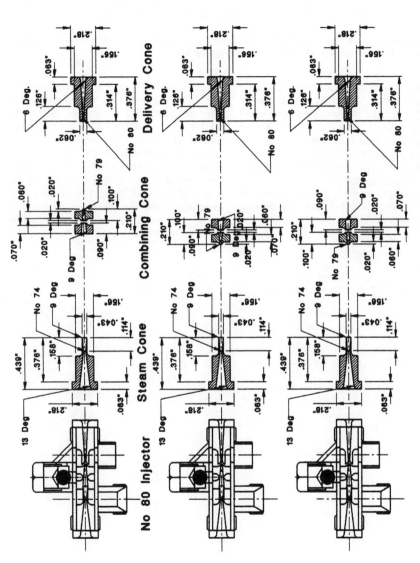

Fig. 6.5 Development of an injector drawing. On the top line the dimensions are settled within the general arrangement so that they fit correctly. On the second line the effect of rotating the view of the combining cone is shown. How much easier this view is to make in the lathe. On the third line the dimensions have been sorted out.

Fig. 6.6 *Copying of one spring coil to form first the top array, then (by mirror imaging) the bottom array and finally half a pitch change by moving the lower array.*

Also note that this is a good example of a drawing which is printed rather larger than full size; this is because of the small dimensions of the details, which are in line with the small font size used. In this case the views are magnified by about 33%, although I printed at 200% full size for my workshop copy.

One further example of the power of copying is shown in Fig. 6.6. To draw a compression spring in cross section the first coil is drawn as a single circle which can then be filled, as described in the next chapter. This counts as two items on the screen, which can be picked up by means of a window or crossing, so that they can be copied the desired number of times at the spring pitch, as in the left-hand view. The second copying operation in the middle view is done by mirror imaging, while the picture is completed as on the right by moving the bottom array of coils by half the pitch.

CHAPTER 7

Hatching and filling

If you consider the amount of time that was involved in manual drawing in hatching and filling, it was certainly a great art and, if done properly, looked very good indeed. Tubal Cain referred in his book to 'laying on a tint' to make a certain item stand out and I well remember from my own experience having to scribe some lines near to the edges of my brand new set squares to act as a spacing guide for drawing cross lines. Then there was the frustration of doing a good piece of sectioning, only to find that it was spoiled by a modification. It was not unknown for some students to wear a hole in their drawing paper with such modifications.

We can put all those problems behind us with CAD, although it is still possible to make a rod for one's own back if the simple rules are not obeyed. The basic rules are: hold back on section shading of all types for as long as possible, since modifications to them are not quite straightforward; keep all such items on their own layer, in the same manner as dimensions or centre-lines.

The technology for inserting the desired patterns is (certainly in the programs available normally to amateurs) not the easiest of facilities to use and it takes up a lot of memory in the computer which could be a disadvantage if you are short of that commodity. Let us consider the facility in two parts: first what is available and second how to apply it.

CAD packages are, of course, not aimed just at mechanical engineering customers, so you will find alongside the engineering hatching symbols all kinds of weird and wonderful patterns from the world of civil engineering as well as architecture. Have a look at these, since some of them may come in useful at odd times. There are brick patterns (anyone for a beam engine?), glazing (cab windows?) and concrete symbols, along with polka dots, stars and even little tufts of grass in some packages! The important thing to remember with all of these patterns that you have at your command is that the scale of them is all important. Study the examples in Figs 7.1 and 7.2. As will be demonstrated you can affect the appearance greatly by altering the scale pitch of lines and items in the hatch, as well as the line thickness as you have seen in the common-all-garden line in a drawing.

The traditional single line of hatch is

Fig. 7.1 *A small selection of the hatch patterns which are available on a CAD package. Note in the top line how the effect changes drastically by altering the scale of the pattern. Top right also shows a 90° rotation. The third row contains dots at different scales and the fourth row two glazing patterns. The whole range of available patterns will normally be found in the handbook.*

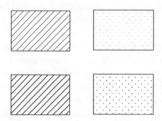

Fig. 7.2 *These two pairs of views contrast the appearance obtained by changing the line thickness.*

obviously the most useful for general sectional work and it can be rotated through 90° if you want to butt two different items up against each other. This rotation must be done before the hatch is drawn in, since like all the settings it cannot be edited after it has appeared on the drawing; if you think about it, 'rotation' means rotation of the item on the drawing and cannot therefore mean changing the rotation of individual bits of that item. Altering the pitch of lines within a hatch and rotation to get the best effect takes a lot of getting used to and you should practise the technique on a quiet corner of the screen before you need it in earnest. See Fig. 7.3.

Several techniques are available for laying down a hatch pattern. The computer will pick up a discreet figure that falls nicely within a window; but that command will tend to pick up some items which you do not want included. So you also have the option of defining the boundaries of a shape which you want to hatch, or you can even point to the objects on the screen which are to form the envelope. Fig. 7.4 gives an example of what can go wrong if you try an incorrect definition of a part to be sectioned. The required result is that drawn in Fig. 7.5 in which the individual hatch areas have been defined by pointing to all the many corners of the view in turn.

You will sometimes want to hatch around an 'island' in a drawing. A way to do this is to define the boundary of the outer shape and then the boundary of the inner shape, the cursor making a single stroke through the area of the hatch pattern. Fig. 7.6 makes this clear. Remember that whenever you define a boundary you have to return a complete loop to enclose the pattern. Having made this recommendation it seems that in the latest version of *Autocad* you can turn

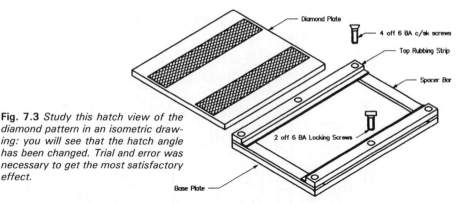

Fig. 7.3 *Study this hatch view of the diamond pattern in an isometric drawing: you will see that the hatch angle has been changed. Trial and error was necessary to get the most satisfactory effect.*

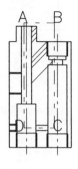

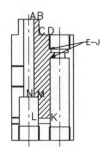

Point in turn to ABCDEFGHIJKLMNA

Fig. 7.4 *In the upper figure an attempt to draw a window around the obvious points fails, as the shape is not defined solely by lines whose ends all meet. The successful attempt in the lower view is made by pointing to all the end points on the boundary (A to N).*

on or off a facility which recognises the presence of an island within a hatch, so that the above procedure is no longer needed.

Hatch patterns cause probably more frustration than any other technique in CAD. By their very nature they are less flexible than most items on the screen and almost any form of editing gives rise to difficulties. Let us look at what happens to a hatch during a mirror image copy: Fig. 7.7 shows a buffer stock in which the top half of the side elevation has been drawn with a view to turning it into a sectional elevation. The view is hatched with lines running upwards from bottom left to top right. When the mirror image is made you will see that the pattern is also reflected, changing its direction, so that it appears to belong to a different part. The only way round this problem is to draw the hatch pattern after the mirror image is struck.

Having had a grumble about some of the difficulties arising from the hatching process, it must be said that it does give very good results when you have mastered it and it is much faster than the old manual process. Some programs discriminate between hatches and fills: with

43

Valve Block

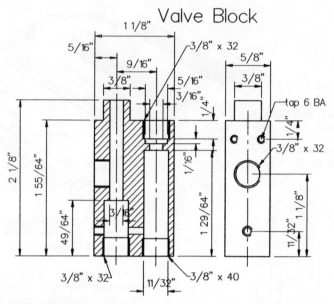

Fig. 7.5 *The desired result of hatching the component in the previous figure. All the individual corners have been pointed to, each hatch area being a separate operation.*

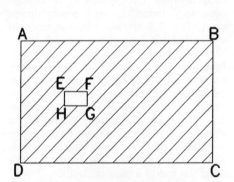

Fig. 7.6 *Having set the hatch pattern parameters, the mouse defines the boundary points in the order: ABCDAEFGHE. In effect this tells the computer that the boundary is the two rectangles on the drawing. Since there is no line AE, the pattern goes across the top left corner without a problem.*

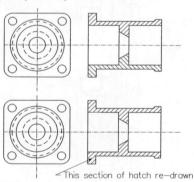

This section of hatch re-drawn

Fig. 7.7 *A buffer with the top half mirrored about the centre-line. Note how the hatch pattern changes to the wrong angle. Lower hatch redrawn in the bottom view.*

44

the latter there are fewer parameters to choose, screen colour being one obvious one that applies also to hatches, but the way of defining the limits of a fill are exactly the same as those already discussed. You will already have seen the results of filling in the balls drawn in Fig. 6.5.

CHAPTER 8

Scaling

Model making is all about manufacturing things to smaller sizes than their originals. In many cases it is possible to measure an original artefact and the notebook will contain the full-size dimensions probably in the form of rough sketches. In other cases the most valuable information may come from makers' drawings, especially general arrangements. Sometimes the initial information is scanty, perhaps some basic dimensions being available and the shape being developed from these data.

This is just the sort of situation where CAD comes into its own. Do not do anything about scaling down and do not worry whether the dimensions are in the same system of measurements that you are working in. Let the computer do the work. Draw out the information full size as far as you can get without going into the fine detail of the job. Then when you are happy that it has reached the stage where you must get down to detail work, issue the instruction to change the scale of the drawing. It is now that you can decide to change between measurement standards and you will see that you will have to compromise to accommodate stock items for machining. Obviously

shaft and screw sizes need to be to recognised standards in a model, although it does not matter if its overall length comes out to an odd value. The power of scaling is best illustrated by two cases from my files.

Firstly, back to the old Gresley tender project: in Fig. 8.1 the works general arrangement drawing provided the dimensions of the key items in the layout and these were all drawn out full size on the CAD system. At a fairly early stage the command was given to shrink the scale by a calculated factor 0.0885. This gives rise, of course, to some odd measurements for such things as wheel centre distances, but this does not matter since the figures are correct to prototype. Details such as axle diameters and buffer stock dimensions have been compromised to fit in with standard threads and stock sizes. The positioning of holes to precise dimensions is straightforward and the manufacture of the whole model has been possible without constant referral to the original drawings once the scale factors have been worked out.

Secondly, an example from one of the *Model Engineering Exhibitions* at which

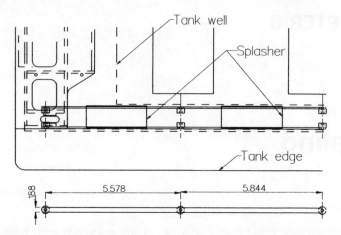

Fig. 8.1 *A detail from the main drawing, plan view of the Gresley tender. The brake gear rods have been projected below the main drawing area and dimensioned, indicating the odd dimensions which sprang from the scaling process after drawing out the wheel centres etc., to full size. There is no problem in machining the parts to these odd dimensions and they are true to prototype.*

I had my computer for demonstration purposes: one of the visitors was interested in old waggons and wished to model one in 16 mm scale. He produced a sketch from the prototype in which he had taken measurements in feet and inches. These dimensions were soon put into the computer and then the scaling command was given to a value of 0.0525, this representing the scale of 16 mm to the ft. The sketch was then dimensioned. In this case the 'customer' had elected to receive the information in metric units, furthermore to two places of decimals for his modelling activities. It can be understood that this facility removes some of the guesswork from the scaling process and certainly all the drudgery. Unfortunately this example was not saved for posterity, it having been erased during one of my 'housekeeping' operations.

It is not difficult to imagine other circumstances where the scaling command is of great benefit. Components are to be dealt with at the appropriate time. Observe too that scaling can be done unevenly in the two machine directions; thus for example a circle can become an ellipse and a square a rectangle. Keep an open mind and the technique will become valuable.

CHAPTER 9

Components

All CAD programs have the facility of a library of components or examples of building blocks. In many instances these will not be just what you want in the type of drawing you are doing, so you should explore the possibilities of creating your own library. Depending on the work which you are doing, you may create many or few components; in my own case perhaps I fail to make as much use of them as I might. Nevertheless they are an invaluable tool for gaining great accuracy without spending much time on detail work.

Let us look in detail at the thorny old problem of drawing nuts and bolts. In days gone by the poor old draughtsman or detailer was instructed to portray great arrays of bolts around all flanges and fittings. Just look at some of the old general arrangement drawings from the public archives to see what a nightmare of a job that was; not content with putting all the fixings in the correct place, some of them had to be broken lines and the line weight had to vary in accordance with their importance.

No wonder that practice in recent years tends to have omitted such niceties from drawings, to cut costs. One big penalty, however, is that there are times when the full implications of sizes and clearances are not taken into account. Have you ever sketched out a flange with its neat ring of fixing holes, only to find that the washers and nuts or bolt-heads come uncomfortably close to the outside diameter on assembly, or even that you have got the bolt heads too close to each other or to some part of the item being drawn?

Let us see how the problem can be tackled. One thing is certain: you do not have to assemble the full range of screw sizes which you use. There is, of course, the odd special case such as the cap-head screw, or the round-head variety, which can be treated in the same way as the example which we are about to tackle, so let us concentrate on the common hexagon-headed screw with its matching nut. In the 'good old days' of Whitworth and BSF screws we were taught that the distance across flats of the hexagon was defined as $1\tfrac{1}{4}$ D + $\tfrac{1}{8}$ in. or some other equally ugly size. Whitworth nuts were bigger than their BSF counterparts but the whole system gradually changed with the general introduction of the Unified series which was to be our defence against the metric system!

Today's head sizes are slightly smaller than their older counterparts, but in the sizes likely to be encountered in model engineering we do not need to worry unduly when drawing them out, so I have taken the BA sizes as an example. In this series the head size across flats is defined as 1.75 x thread diameter. This is the basis on which to work. What we are going to do is to draw an imaginary set of screws to 1 in. thread diameter and then scale them accordingly. In the first figure is drawn a set of screw thread views dimensioned so that you can copy them (Fig. 9.1). This is the set which I store in my component library under the remarkable acronym 'Nutsbolt'. The reason there are four views side by side is that at the time I wish to draw a fixing view I may not know whether I want a nut, a bolt or in plan or elevation. So here they are, complete with centre-lines and with the dimensions which you will need if you want to copy the idea.

Let us now consider how to proceed if we want the end view of a 4 BA nut.

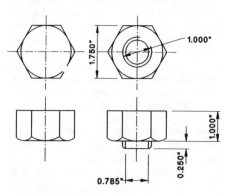

Fig 9.1 *The basic screw shapes drawn down from my component library, with dimensions added.*

Refer to Fig. 9.2. We call down from the component library the component in question, placing it on the correct layer and well clear of the drawing, say to the right-hand side. On many CAD packages you will have a ghosting facility, so that when a component or other item is being planted into place a ghost image is produced before it is clicked home, so that you can make sure that it is going into the correct position. From the cluster of views placed out of the way we can delete the unwanted items, or even move some of them for future use on a related part. Do not forget the power of the **window** or **crossing** commands for picking up or leaving out say the centre-lines. Now a 4 BA screw is 0.141 in. in diameter, so we can now use the **scale** command to be found in every program: instruct the system that the items in the window should be reduced to a scale of 0.141 in both X and Y directions and you have a component of the right size in a fraction of the time which it would have taken to draw it.

It now only remains to pick up the centre of the component by snapping to that point and then moving it lock stock and barrel to the desired point in the drawing. If you have deleted all the unwanted parts of the component display, the outside boundary of the drawing will return to that which it was originally. The array can be completed by copying the component for multiple screw positions. This reinforces the significance of the layer method for ease of editing, since a layer containing only the screw images may be edited without any risk to other items already on the drawing.

Obviously with such a powerful method at your disposal you can give any amount of embellishment you wish to detail components, even shading the parts in imaginary shade, and certainly

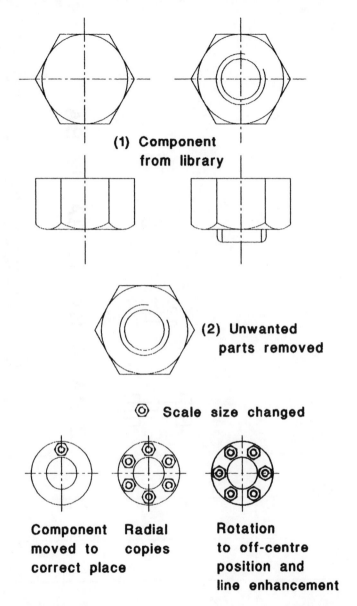

(1) Component from library

(2) Unwanted parts removed

Scale size changed

Component moved to correct place

Radial copies

Rotation to off-centre position and line enhancement

Fig. 9.2 *We require six 4 BA screws around the flange in the bottom LH corner. The steps are: (1) bring down the components out of harm's way (2) erase unwanted parts (3) reduce the scale to the 4 BA size (a factor of 0.141) (4) move the small component to the correct PCD, copy an array around the centre point, rotate all to the correct off-centres position and embolden the lines as required.*

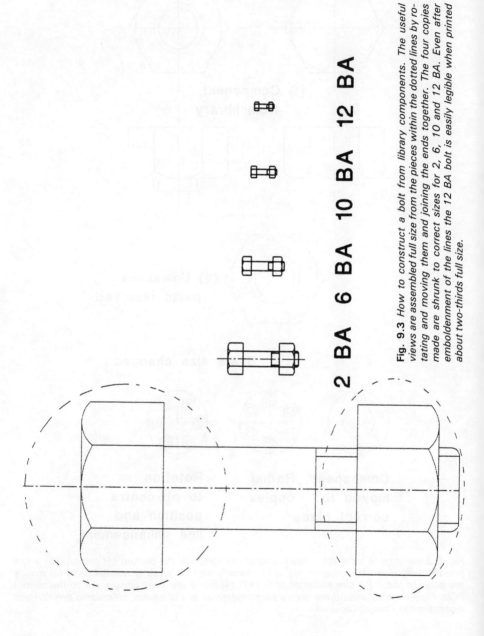

Fig. 9.3 How to construct a bolt from library components. The useful views are assembled full size from the pieces within the dotted lines by rotating and moving them and joining the ends together. The four copies made are shrunk to correct sizes for 2, 6, 10 and 12 BA. Even after emboldenment of the lines the 12 BA bolt is easily legible when printed about two-thirds full size.

2 BA   6 BA   10 BA   12 BA

nicely rounding and filleting the corners. You will furthermore appreciate the power at your disposal for any size or convention, an M6 screw merely being called up by a scale factor of 0.236.

The other example (see Fig. 9.3), given in printed form shows how legibility is preserved even after much reduction: a 12 BA screw is only 0.051 in. dia, nevertheless its lines are clear apart from those forming the screw thread itself. If this aspect worries you then do not embolden the lines before printing and the discrimination will be preserved down to a smaller size. This sort of thing is obviously down to personal preference.

From the rather expansive treatment of the ubiquitous screw you will see the value of components. Assemble them by drawing only once such things as rivets, pipe fittings, springs, bearings or whatever subjects you find the most useful. What I hope has been given is a taste of what you can do to save time compared with the traditional drawing procedure.

Another suggestion for a useful component is the symbol representing the first or third angle projection which should be placed at the bottom right-hand corner of drawings. See Fig. 9.4 for the first angle example. You can combine this with a title box, logo, or whatsoever you will which can then be called down easily from the component file within the CAD program, thus ensuring a

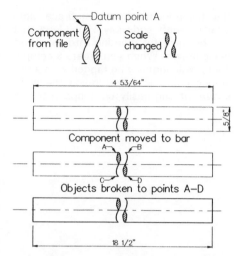

Line widths enhanced and dimension edited

Fig. 9.5 *Break line assembly for standard long shaft convention and the suggested way of applying it to the middle of a ⅝ in. dia shaft. The reference point is snapped to the shaft at a suitable position. Each shaft object is then broken and snapped back (or trimmed) to the stub ends of the component.*

fair degree of uniformity among your drawings.

A further idea is the break line for solid shafts, which should be stored as a 1 in. dia component which can then easily be scaled to suit any application. The form is indicated in Fig. 9.5. It is recommended that the line thicknesses be drawn to suit your normal finished standard ie enhanced principal lines but minimum thickness for the hatchings. It is likely that the component as reproduced will all be on one layer, so you may consider changing parts of it such as the hatchings. Do this operation before scaling and applying it to the shaft. To draw the curved end shapes a Bezier curve is used. It is suggested that

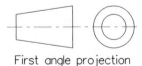

First angle projection

Fig. 9.4 *The first angle projection symbol for saving as a component.*

the component should embrace stub straight shaft ends say ⅛ in. long that can be used for planting into the shaft being drawn. When you create a component it will normally be tagged with a reference point; if this is made the point shown, it can easily be snapped to the mating item on the drawing, after scaling to the size required and rotating if necessary to the correct angle.

I can see no reasonable way of extending this process to that for a hollow shaft, because the inner diameter bears no relationship to the outer one.

CHAPTER 10

Drawing text and presentation of drawings

This section is included before the chapter on dimensioning because it is essential to understand the facilities which are available before you start to use them for dimensioning purposes. For instance font selection and sizing occur in both areas and there is the opportunity to get things right from the start and to avoid unnecessary work later.

Text passages may be laid down on a drawing for labelling, specification and titling purposes, but do not look for the versatility of a word processor within your CAD package. You will find some frustrations, although with the continued development of the software programs one would expect some of these to disappear.

Fonts

Every program gives you a choice of various fonts, not necessarily the same as those in word processors. Some will suit disciplines such as architecture, but trying to focus on model engineering we should be considering what is best for those sorts of drawing. The basic font available when the package is set up may be labelled such as **Engineer** and is a rather nondescript and ugly form, nevertheless ideally suited to reproduction by a standard plotter. There are some much more acceptable fonts available in most programs and some of these are illustrated in Fig. 10.1 to make some points about their reproduction and general appearance. Some plotters may not reproduce what seems like a common font, or they may change various letters or even spacing, so check before it is too late what your equipment will cope with. In general if you use a printer there should be no problem.

Engineer   Roman S

Helvetica   **Palatin**

Roman C   **Times Roman**

Fig. 10.1 *These six fonts are all printed to the same size, although some appear bigger than others. You will note that some are serif types, that is to say they contain curlicues at the ends of their strokes. For this reason they should not be used on engineering drawings, since in dimension work clarity of the figures is not improved.*

55

As with drawing lines you have the opportunity to alter the weight of the letters in the styles which comprise single or double lines and in those fonts you can fill in the spaces between the lines to form a bold typeface. This is not necessarily true for the well known 'designer' fonts such as **Helvetica**, where even the thickness ratios are precisely defined. The exact form of what is available varies according to the program, so you are advised to experiment with the fonts before committing them to an important drawing. Remember too that if you are doing work for publication in one of the magazines the editor may have definite preferences which should be heeded.

Text size is a parameter which can be varied; unlike the practice in word processing you do not choose a size in 'points' and there is no standard preference offered. You have to make a judgement according to the finished size of the drawing and even the amount of space which is available for the text. As a guide, if you envisage printing full size then start off with a font size of ⅛ in. If it is going to be a large drawing you will have to enlarge the size accordingly. Although you can always apply a scaling factor as you will have done in components, such a move planned deliberately is not recommended since it can play havoc with the general layout of the sheet. As another rule, text will look best if it is kept clear of the drawing lines themselves.

The font designer will have thought out carefully the shape and spacing of the letters and this will be his standard form. In order to make things fit into confined spaces, however, it may be possible to alter the width of the letters in proportion to their height, known as the aspect ratio. This should, however, be done only in exceptional circum- stances as it normally does nothing for the legibility of the work. It is also possible to slope the letters to form italics. This is bad practice in engineering drawings and is to be eschewed!

In the writing of text lines on drawings, as the process is known, you should use the normal upper and lower case letters; do not attempt to print everything in upper case letters, as this looks amateurish and reduces legibility, besides wasting space. For a correct and incorrect illustration see Fig. 10.2.

Note the different styles of font which can be printed; my own preference is for **Helvetica** or **Roman-S**, which are both

Notes:
Decking to be built either side of door to height of 900mm, with an upper deck at the rear raised up 450. At the back of the court the main decking drops to 750 high and there is an upper deck along the short wall.

All horizontal surfaces should be covered with blue cloth, which is draped down to join the lower level or floor.

NOTES:
DECKING TO BE BUILT EITHER SIDE OF DOOR TO HEIGHT OF 900mm, WITH AN UPPER DECK AT THE REAR RAISED UP 450. AT THE BACK OF THE COURT THE MAIN DECKING DROPS TO 750 HIGH AND THERE IS AN UPPER DECK ALONG THE SHORT WALL.

ALL HORIZONTAL SURFACES SHOULD BE COVERED WITH BLUE CLOTH, WHICH IS DRAPED DOWN TO JOIN THE LOWER LEVEL OR FLOOR.

Fig. 10.2 *This illustrates the right and wrong way to write text. In this case an extract is lifted from a set of specifications written for an exhibition stand holding locomotive models. Note how much easier it is to read the lower case message, rather than that in all capital letters. These extracts are written in the same font size – the upper case example just wastes paper! If it used to excess, underlining also impairs legibility.*

plain or sans serif types. But one word of warning: you will find that the more complicated fonts slow down the process considerably, especially when it comes to recalling and redrawing views. As computers get faster this becomes less and less of a problem, but one way I used to get over the problem before my own machine was updated was to write everything in a simple font such as **Engineer** and then change the font setting at the last moment before printing, at the same time as emboldening the lines. This certainly saved frustration but it may be found that by changing the font you alter some of the clearances within the dimension envelopes, because different fonts take up different line lengths for the same message.

Presentation

Many drawings, especially those produced in company drawing offices, are enclosed in a border and may have an area for logo, organisation name, date, approval and other bits of red tape. Most of these fripperies are of no use in our surroundings, although if you wish to communicate with others it is certainly worth putting the projection definition and perhaps your name and date and copyright symbol in the bottom right-hand corner with space for drawing title and number if desired. The easiest way of handling these pieces of information is by fashioning them into a component, which can be called up before the drawing is finished. The previous remarks apply here concerning scaling, although in the case of a drawing which is to be printed at a reduced size, the component will have to be *increased* in scale to make it stand out.

Although the individual details of laying down text lines vary between programs, as a general rule you should align text to the left of the presentation point and the length of lines should suit the job being done. Mistakes can be edited out in the usual way after the line is laid down, but you will find that the editing process is nowhere near as flexible as in the word processor, so try to get things right first time. One useful tip if you want to make a line of items of text across the page: use the snap grid facility to anchor the starting points of all the entries.

Neat and methodical text lines can make or mar an otherwise good presentation.

CHAPTER 11

Dimensioning

This is where the CAD system comes into its own as a time saver, but at the same time if you have not obeyed the rules of accuracy then you will find the pitfalls. As stated earlier, the computer records things to a standard of accuracy greater than that required for most engineering practice. In my earliest days of playing with the system the commonest trap into which I fell was failing to start a line accurately from the point at the end of the previous object. This basically boiled down to finger trouble, using the wrong button of the mouse to start an object. Now this is perhaps a function of the particular program with which I am working, but every package has its own peculiarities and you will soon find out the blind spot in the one you have chosen. Certainly looking at the pages of the magazines there is evidence to suggest that not everyone who uses a CAD package does so in such a way which allows it to do the dimensioning without human intervention. Inevitably the following methods draw heavily on my own experience using *Generic CADD*, but the principles are the same in whatever system you are using.

Irrespective of how many digits you have used to input the data, when it comes to the dimensioning process the computer will display any number of digits up to its maximum ability. Furthermore, it is quite capable of switching between fractions and decimals and even of translating between imperial and metric units. Thus, for example, if you have drawn a line to a length of $4\frac{7}{16}$ in., this may be dimensioned as just that, or as 4.438, or even as 4.43750 in. Remember that the accuracy cannot be improved during the dimensioning process, so be consistent with your drawing in anticipation of the dimensioning results which you hope to achieve.

It is necessary first to choose the font with which you wish to work, which should be the same as that used for captions and other lines of text. Dimensions *must* always be placed upon their own layer which should not be used for any other purpose. The CAD program will handle this problem itself after you have defined which layer that should be. For some obscure reason I choose Layer 3 as the dimension layer and I am the first to admit that it does tend to get in the way of the layer stack as it builds up in a complicated drawing. But as long as you remember what you are doing there should be no problem. Always use the thinnest lines for the dimension system and choose white lines for a black screen and vice versa. Even if you are printing in colour on your printer such lines will always print in black.

Now to size of dimensions, this depends entirely on how you see the drawing being displayed and the small details of the lines themselves. You must have an idea of the overall size and scale of things that will give you a clue about the size of print which you can expect. For example, a small workshop device will almost certainly print out full size, although if it is to be reproduced some magazine editors may have other ideas of cramming it into a corner of one of their pages. The good news is that the font size may be considerably smaller than that which you would have used in manual drawing and still be legible. As a guide, ⅛ in. font height works well in full-size printing and you can even reduce this to ¹⁄₁₆ in. if you have drawn out very small details with lots of dimensions to come. At the other end of the scale, if you are laying out your new workshop think in terms of at least ¾ in. letters for a print of 1 in. to the foot. Another way of looking at it is that a double-ended grinder has a footprint size of 15 in. x 9 in. and a label placed on it with ¾ in. letters would not look out of place. It is most important to get the font sizing right before you start the dimensioning process, since alterations at a later date are very frustrating.

The next thing to settle is the dimension line arrow. Get the style right for engineering drawings. A filled arrow of very acute angle (10 degrees) is the only one really acceptable (see Fig. 11.1). Nothing looks more amateurish than a splayed arrow, or one of the many fancy

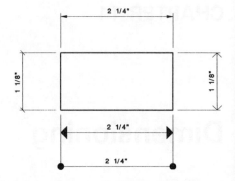

Fig. 11.1 *This shows the only acceptable form of dimension arrow at the top. All other forms look ridiculous! The correct angle is 10 degrees, the arrows are filled and their size is similar to the font size.*

options offered in the menu, which may be acceptable in other fields of drawing. It is easy to select arrows outside or inside the extension lines, depending on the relative size of the dimension to the gap into which it fits. You will also find a choice of whether or not you wish to display each arrow. The normal choice of course is to elect to display everything, but watch out for the mouse movement which may lead you to hide one of the desired items inadvertently.

Another choice before you is for fixed centreing of the text or a display that can be moved across the dimension line before finally anchoring the figures. I would always choose the flexibility offered you; centreing by eye is acceptable.

Deciding on the format of the display ought to be simple. There is an easy facility for changing between fractions and decimals and I use the former for non-critical dimensions, changing to 3 places of decimals for the more precise dimensions. Remember that stock material should be called for by its fractional

60

size (viz ½ in. bar or ⁷/₁₆ in. hex) unless a bastard size is required such as those for the BA screws. If you are working in metric units, stock sizes and non-critical dimensions should be shown as plain mm., although occasionally you may have to resort to one place of decimals (viz 5.5 mm silver steel). But where you are specifying critical dimensions, two places of decimals is right.

Correct practice is to precede a figure less than 1 by a zero. This option is available on the setting up menu. However, there is an argument to which I subscribe that for small components with many such dimensions the leading zero may be omitted; it can just lead to too much clutter. The other choice for which you have a rational option is whether to display the system mark on all dimensions, thus (") for imperial and (mm) for metric display. All other things being equal the correct practice is to display the system mark on all dimensions, but again the drawing may become too cluttered for comfort and the choice is yours. If you change your mind at a later stage you will find a procedure for making simple alterations to what you have already chosen.

One departure from best practice which you will have to tolerate is the way the computer writes fractions. Tubal Cain was adamant that fractions should be written with small figures separated by a horizontal line. The computer thinks otherwise and the CAD packages with which I am familiar all use a slash designation to divide the numerator from the denominator. Whether or not you approve you are stuck with this and one advantage is that it probably makes small figures more legible. But do be careful with the proportions of the dimension system: it is in such circumstances that it is very useful to be able to choose the alignment of the text within the dimension line, rather than always have it centred. Refer back to Fig. 6.5 as a good example of how legibility can be improved by careful alignment and even by choosing a different font. Many of these dimensions have been moved outside the dimension extension lines to improve legibility.

Before leaving the text display the other option is the position of the figures relative to the dimension line (called the offset). They must be *above* the line and should be separated by a distance of about 30 to 50% of the font height. A little trial and error will get things looking satisfactory.

Having settled the parameters relating to the display of figures and dimension line, it still remains to decide those for the extension lines. You will find offset and overlap values called for in the set-up menu. Basically the gap (or offset) between the job and the end of the dimension line extension should be of the order of half to two-thirds of the font height, but make it to look right. You can also instruct the dimension extension to overlap the end of the dimension line, by at least that amount in both directions, the two different entries being needed to take into account some times when the dimension line is brought up the 'wrong' side of the drawing, in which case you may want the extension to project a slightly different distance than normal.

The usual procedure in model engineering is to call for each dimension to stand alone, so be aware of the facility that is available to **stack** dimensions. This is more appropriate in the production engineering environment.

Writing the dimensions

Now at long last we can look forward to seeing the dimensions appear at the click of the mouse. Another choice for the display is whether the writing should be all horizontal or aligned with the dimension. Choose the latter. Give the instruction to write an horizontal dimension. Snap to the two points whose distance apart is required and you will be prompted with the value of the display. You can then move the dimension around above or below the drawing by a variable amount provided that you have elected for a non-fixed proximity. When you think that it looks in the right position, a click of the mouse works wonders and the

dimension appears like magic. Fig. 11.2 shows a well-dimensioned drawing.

There is another set of commands headed **dimension move** and this is sensitive to the position on the dimension which you choose. For instance, if you point to the dimension line near one of the arrows, you will be able to lengthen or shorten the extension lines, whereas if you point to the dimension figures you will be able to move the figures along the dimension line itself.

Another command which you should practise is **dimension change**. Not only

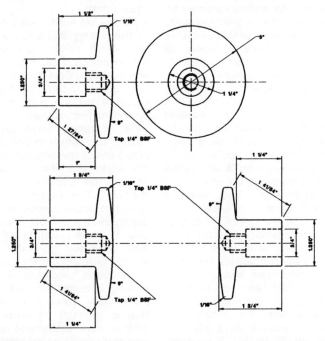

Fig. 11.2 *A well-dimensioned drawing. Points to note in the top view are the alignment of all the length dimensions with their dimension lines, the omission of the dimension line for the 9 in. radius and the horizontal alignment of the dimension figures of the diameter and radius dimensions. In the bottom left view the top elevation is repeated and stretched: note how even the dimensions adhere to their new values. Rotation of the view after dimensioning preserves the dimensions albeit in different attitudes in the lower right view.*

does this enable you to edit the text of the dimension, it also provides the facility to change all the settings from font and arrow size to the offset values. Thus at the early stages of a drawing it gives you the opportunity to experiment with the settings until you are satisfied with your results. It is good use of time to concentrate on the horizontal dimensions as a batch before going on to the vertical ones, but the same remarks apply to these. You should really master the quick way to change arrows from inside to outside to enable you to cope with small distances. You can now put all the principal dimensions on the drawing and they should be clearly displayed. Remember what has been said about moving parts around on a drawing to give plenty of space for comfort. Do not forget to turn on the dimension layer if you are moving things around, otherwise it can get left behind!

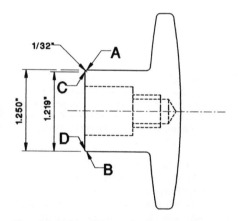

Fig. 11.3 *Possible confusion because of a small radius on the corners. The outer dimension is correct, the mouse having clicked to points A and B. In the inner dimension an error has come about by pointing to points C and B. Careful alignment of the mouse is important.*

When you are pointing to objects as the targets of dimensioning beware of the edge effects. For instance, if there are two points close together make sure you are snapping to the right one. Confusion can arise if there is a small fillet on a corner; that fillet will have two discreet ends and, depending on how the mouse is aligned with the end of the line, it is possible to pick up the wrong end of the fillet as in Fig. 11.3. In all the dimensioning work you must make sure that you snap to the correct points at all times.

Master the horizontal and vertical dimensioning process before going further and then try dimensioning at an angle and then **aligned**. Dimensioning at an angle is self-explanatory: it is particularly useful in isometric projections where you can set the angle to 30° and −30°. The dimensions will then be the correct ones for the projection axes which you have drawn. See Fig. 11.4.

An aligned dimension is one which measures the shortest distance between two points, not necessarily placed on the same axis. You cannot use this facility for normal measurement since for much of the time the required points will be out of line and you would obtain a false figure. An aligned dimension is put into Fig. 11.2 as an example, although it does not serve any useful purpose for manufacture.

Continuing with the facilities available, diameters are designated with an arrow at each end and a line extended from one of them as far as you wish to pull it. Make sure that the **orthogonal discipline** is turned off so that you can adjust the angle of the dimension line as required. In order to display the dimension correctly it is necessary to adjust the instruction for writing the text display from **aligned** to **horizontal** (see examples in Fig. 11.2). This is irksome in this

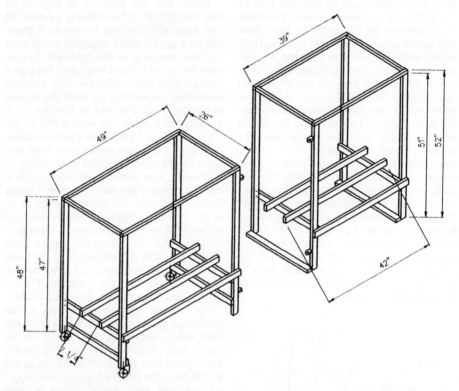

Fig. 11.4 *This illustrates the dimensioning of an isometric view of a storage frame made from steel hollow section. An A3 size print was more than adequate for workshop use during construction, but this small version gives the right flavour. One criticism I have of the program is the curious angles at which the dimension extensions are displayed. I have not found the way around this problem but it is a small price to pay for what is otherwise a very clear display.*

particular program, but some people may have overcome it by another method. Similar remarks apply to the dimensioning of arcs of a circle, in which the dimensioning line springs from the arc centre. There may be occasions when this is unacceptable, such as when there is only a short section of arc used and the dimension line going all the way would not look right. In such cases simply alter the conditions to turn off (or hide) the dimension line.

The displaying of angles is one feature which is not ideal. After experimentation you may decide to reduce or even hide the dimension lines, but here are some tips from personal experience. You have to start by defining the angle, starting with its centre point and going on to each of its two rays (see Fig. 11.5). As you position the display the length of the ghosted image on the screen may indicate that it is flipping from the required value to its double complement, for example 90° could flip to 270° as the cursor moves around the screen. Considerable practice is required to get satisfaction in this display and I regard this technique as one of the least satisfactory of the whole program. In moving the angular display round after the position has been set has some significant constraints applied to it. If you are displaying dimensions to 3 places of decimals, the same accuracy will appear on angular dimensions unless you change the decimal display to 0 places. Another point to note in the package which I use: it is impossible in normal practice to move the text of an angular dimension outside the dimension line. One way which I

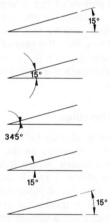

Fig. 11.5 *Displaying angles – from top to bottom (1) arrows inside (2) arrows outside (3) dimension block moved outside lines before positioning in which the angle flips to [360-15] and (4) dimension lines hidden with the text moved around from the second example. In (5) the first display has been exploded and the dimension label has then been moved to its new position.*

have used to get around this one is by 'kidding' the system that the text is longer than it really is and adding a load of blank spaces in front of the dimension, so that when it is moved the blank spaces alter the apparent alignment of the dimension. Another way to overcome the problem of an intractable dimension assembly is to explode it, after which the offending portion can be moved in the same way as any other item, but of course it can no longer be edited in the normal manner.

The final set of dimensions to master is the leader, or the only dimension which is set by hand. The arrow pointing to the required place is of the same shape as the normal arrow. You will be invited to write the words or figures you require and then to define the start point of the leader. You can stretch it as far as you wish, and then align the wording to the left or to the right. There is another adjustment to be made, which is the length of the leader shoulder, the horizontal bit of line joining the words to the dimension line. This can be tested by 'changing' the leader setting after writing the first one and this change can be incorporated into the dimension settings menu. Some programs have facilities to make leaders to reach around corners, so it would pay you to 'get to know your leader'.

Displaying limits

Facilities also exist in most CAD programs for displaying tolerances automatically, but this is really for the commercial engineering shop, not for the model engineering hobby. I put this in the category of fun to play with, nevertheless it warrants a short demonstration since there are some circumstances such as bearing fits where we must take limits

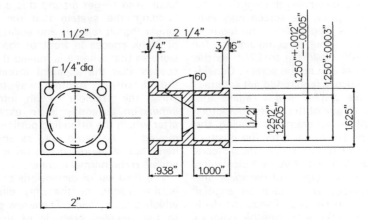

Fig. 11.6 *The buffer stock which we met before has had limits applied to the bore for the buffer to enter. Only the left-hand display of limits is really satisfactory.*

seriously. You will find that your program menu gives you some options, including the one which you will already be familiar with, that of not displaying tolerances. The way the system normally works is that you are asked for the upper and lower tolerance, for example the female socket into which a buffer fits should be between 5 and 12 tenths of a thou over the nominal size, so you can give the system these two figures. When you set the tolerance band any dimension which you draw will have the limits displayed in one of several forms which meet the correct drawing-office practice. Fig. 11.6 clearly illustrates the ways in which the figures can be displayed, three options in my program being the maximum/minimum values, stacked tolerances and fixed band tolerance. As far as I am concerned only the first of these three really does what is required; the stacked tolerance insists on making the upper and lower limits of opposite sign, not necessarily what is required. The fixed band tolerance is alright only if you

happen to draw the item being detailed right in the middle of the tolerance band. You will note that in the case of the nominal value display this can conform to the level to which the rest of the drawing is displayed, that is to 3 places of decimals, although the tolerance band is to 4 places.

Breaking the rules

Most drawings should be produced to a high standard, obeying all the rules, but there are occasions when it is good to depart from them. I recall drawing out the coordinates for drilling hundreds of holes in my set of tender frames, see Fig. 11.7. I established a datum point at the top centre from which all dimensions were to be struck. There was no point in showing both arrow heads, nor the dimension lines; moreover the rule about alignment was broken by putting the figures in line with the arrows instead of above them. Sticking to the normal rules would have detracted from the clarity

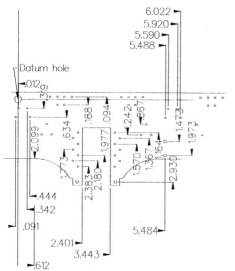

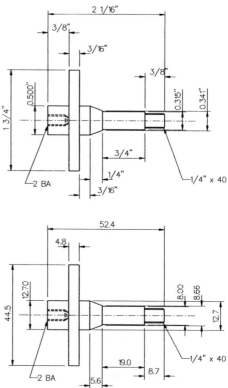

Fig. 11.8 *One drawing, but two sets of dimensions, each on its own layer.*

Fig 11.7 *A small section from a tender frame machining drawing, showing how the rules can be broken in appropriate circumstances. Datum hole top left, dimension lines omitted, figures aligned with arrows and " marks not shown.*

and if you consider what is required in such circumstances, it is more a list of map references than a first-class engineering drawing.

The other example from life refers to the facility which the computer has for converting between imperial and metric standards. At a *Model Engineer Exhibition* several years ago I was asked to draw out a small mandrel from a sketch on the back of the SMEE chairman's cigarette packet. This gave some basic inch dimensions and being familiar with the Quorn grinder into which the mandrel had to fit I had no difficulty in interpreting the sketch and turning it into a well-dimensioned drawing. "Oh", said the Chairman, "but the lathe is metric"....
Two-second pause for a decision. I merely hid Layer 3 and turned on another layer, rejigged the screen display in metric, with the dimension display to two places of decimals. The metric dimensions can be turned on or off at will, hiding one or other of the two dimension layers, as in Fig. 11.8.

CHAPTER 12

Some ideas for speedy operation

Scale rulers – make CAD work for you

One of the things that model engineering is all about is reproducing original arte-facts to small size. Sometimes it is possible to measure the original object, for instance in a museum, and at other times the information is available solely on old drawings or even photographs. Which-ever source of information you are working from, it may be a good idea to produce a scale ruler especially for the purpose. I well remember producing scale rulers manually in the past, employ-ing the well-known technique on the drawing board which involved starting with two oblique lines on the sheet at an angle whose cosine is the reduction ratio required. It is laborious and produces a scale ruler which is then as vulnerable as any other piece of paper or cardboard. It

is far easier with CAD and produces copy which can easily be reproduced if it gets damaged or oily. This is an exercise in copying, lettering, editing and scaling; with reference to Fig. 12.1, this is how I go about the task for a ruler with 1/10 in. graduations.

Decide how long you would like the finished ruler to be and allow a little lee-way. This accounts for the rectangular boundary which is the first thing to draw. A convenient size of rectangle is 12 in. x 1 in. Next at ½ in. from the top left corner draw a vertical line ⅜ in. long, as the baseline. Copy this line ten times at 1 in. intervals to give the main inch graduations.

Next, moving in another ½ in. from the start point, draw a line ¼ in. long as the first half-inch marker and repeat this line by copying it 9 times at 1 in. intervals to form all the other half inch graduations.

Fig. 12.1 *A 10 in. scale length scale ruler with 1/10 in. graduations, reduced in this example to a 40% full-size scale.*

Follow this by drawing the first ⅒ in. graduation just ⅛ in. long alongside the zero mark; copy this short line 3 times at ⅒ in. intervals and then make a further copying operation, this time on all four small marks, 19 times using say the 0 mark as the datum point and the ½ in. mark as the reference point for the second set of copies. You will gather from this move that it is not necessary to choose a reference point that has anything to do with the items being copied. What you are doing is to move items around the drawing by an absolute distance, so if you can make use of a set of reference data somewhere else on the screen, use them.

The scale should now be complete and ready for lettering. Go up in line thickness for writing the letters and figures. I think it is easiest to position the first figure, 0, and then to copy it 10 times and finally to edit each figure to the correct value. During these operations you should depart from the customary convention followed in most engineering drawings, which is to justify the text to the left. In these number graduations the text should be centred and this command is one which you should find within the text setting menu in your program. So you should have a row of eleven 0s sitting in the correct place just below the graduations. Edit each bit of text in turn to produce the correct figures; if you have followed the advice about centre justification you will notice that when it comes to editing the final one to read 10, this value will sit perfectly symmetrically about its graduation line.

So we now have a screen full of ruler which the computer interprets as a 10 in. scale. A wise procedure is to mark it with the identification as indicated, since you will probably amass more than one different scale over the years and it is a pity if they get mixed up. It now remains to alter the scale of the drawing in accordance with the workshop requirement, an operation with which you will be very familiar. Before preparing to print the scale, copy it several times at close range: you might as well fill the A4 sheet on which you are going to print, since when you cut the scale out of the paper the rest will not be of much use for anything.

Multiple leaders

You may wish to label several items with the same leader, that is to say to write one dimension or instruction and print from it more than one arrow and leader line. I have not seen in the instructions for a program an explicit way of carrying out such an operation, but here is my suggested solution.

Let us say that we wish to tag three holes with the label 'Tap 4 BA'. As in Fig. 12.2 apply the full leader to the top hole, making sure that it is positioned in such a way that it is easily accessible to the other positions. Such a leader will have a dimension line springing from the arrow

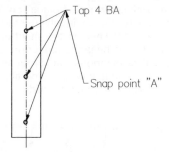

Fig. 12.2 *Three leaders with the same message of text. Only the top one contains the writing and the other two are snapped to the point 'A'.*

and a shoulder pointing towards the message. The junction of these two lines is a point to which you should be able to snap. The second and further leaders should merely have their text messages left blank, but when you are asked to enter the positions of the leaders, snap them to the line junction mentioned above. This procedure removes any risk arising from overwriting and still allows you to edit the leader text at some future occasion without having to separate out the overlaid items.

The odd fiddle!

You should find that the examples given in this book get you off to a fine start with your chosen CAD package, but it is good to describe an odd unconventional movement and to discuss its implications. Let us suppose that we are fitting a compression spring to a bobbin as shown in Fig. 12.3. We could possibly

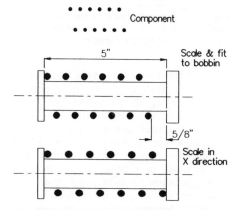

Fig. 12.3 *A component representing a compression spring is scaled to fit on to a bobbin, with six whole turns. The spring on its own layer is too short, so its scale is changed in the X direction only so that it fits the space available.*

have produced already as a component a section of spring. I personally like to fill such an item to make it stand out. The drawing shows how the component is scaled to the correct diameter for the job, but I have contrived that it is too short to fill the bobbin drawn and I do not wish to increase the number of turns. It is no good considering a stretching operation, since that does not space things out in the way which we require. We could move each coil in turn, or even erase all but two and re-copy the whole array. However, there is the alternative of altering the scale in one axis only.

The dimensions given in the upper view show that the spring is short by a factor of 5/4.375, or 1.143. The spring components are of course on their own layer, so we can inhibit the other layers for the editing operation that follows. Choose the **scale change** command and enclose the whole of the spring items within a window. You should then be asked to state the new scale for both the X and Y axes, so enter the factor 1.143 for the X axis only and 1.000 for the Y axis. The new array of coils should just fill the gap available. If the datum point is chosen as the extreme left end of the coils, all the expansion will take place to the right.

One of the quirks of this method is that a circle remains a circle when either of its axes is stretched, so I have drawn the spring coils as ellipses, whose major and minor axes are of virtually the same length. Failure to make a minute difference will not produce a successful ellipse, since the computer realises that it is really a circle. It is almost as easy to draw an ellipse as a circle, so that is what you see in front of you. Close scrutiny will reveal that the scaling operation has in fact elongated the ellipses, but the result does not offend.

This example is given not so much as a recommended way of editing a drawing but rather to show what can be achieved if you are in a tight corner.

Dimension tampering

Another fiddle with which you should be familiar is the editing of dimensions. You should find the **dimension edit** command within your program menu and this enables you to change the wording, or even fake a value for something that it is not! Fig. 12.4 gives an example where there is a 2 BA tapped hole with a short counterbore; we should imagine a space constraint which precludes the normal use of a leader for such purposes. If you do choose to edit a dimension in such a way as this, you should be aware of a pitfall: should you further 'change' the dimension, possibly by altering its format, the original true value could be reimposed in the dimension space.

Cutting and chopping

You will have noticed in a number of places within this book I have used real live examples from my files. In many cases it has been unnecessary or indeed unhelpful to show the whole picture, so a scrap view is the order of the day. A good example was the dimensioning spread shown in Fig. 11.7. That represents only a tiny portion of the whole drawing which is over two feet long. When this was chosen as an example, the area selected was picked out by means of a crossing that enclosed just over the items which are now visible in the figure. Lines such as the extremities of the frame were still showing to a much greater length than that required and these were cut back to the desired level using the **trim** command. In some circum-

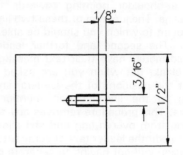

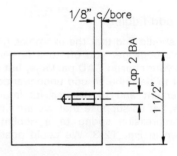

Fig. 12.4 *The upper view is correctly dimensioned. In the lower view one of the dimensions has been edited manually.*

stances the **trim** and **extend** commands are a little fickle especially on a complicated drawing, so it is sometimes useful to draw a temporary construction line to act as a 'target' place where the trimming operation is to end. By such means it is possible to transfer information from one drawing to another. Remember it is often possible to load more than one drawing into the memory without having to unload the one not being actively displayed on the screen. Should this not be possible you can save the desired area of amended drawing as a component and then operate on it when the desired drawing is on the screen.

CHAPTER 13

Projection and development

Projection in CAD

In his original book on workshop drawing Tubal Cain went to some lengths to explain the theory of drawing projection. It does, of course, explain the way in which the different views are assembled and how it is possible to make one view by combining the information contained in others. There may well be instances when projection methods are useful, especially where you are trying to interpret scant information contained within an old general arrangement drawing.

It is easy to perform projections in CAD. There are no dividers to worry about and no pencil lines to have to erase at a later stage. Provided that snapping is performed in the proper fashion perfect accuracy is guaranteed and the method is quick.

In the example given in Fig. 13.1 I have copied the original sketch used as an illustration by Tubal Cain, since it demonstrates the principles well. A small notched block is shown in plan view at A, in which the dimensions are specified of the outside shape and the positions of the ends of the oblique wedge. Projections are indicated in the two directions

(i) and (iii) which define the other views. It is helpful to draw the 45-degree reflection line to which it is easy to get the mouse to snap. Also indicated are two of the circular arcs which denote the process of 'turning' the view through 90 degrees. It is quite unnecessary to make use of these arcs, they just serve to illustrate the principle. On the view B you will see that it is necessary to specify two other dimensions, although the height at the left-hand end of the wedge would be superfluous. To complete the front elevation C it is essential to project from both the other views; such is the essence of projection.

In drawing out the part I have included all the projection lines, but with the tracking or anchoring procedure being available within the CAD package these lines are not necessary. It is prudent, however, to draw a 45-degree line such as the one shown but it should be erased before the drawing is finished.

In such a simple illustration as this it is quite unnecessary to draw the third view, but the principles are there and may be found useful in the real world where more detail is available and only properly displayed on another view.

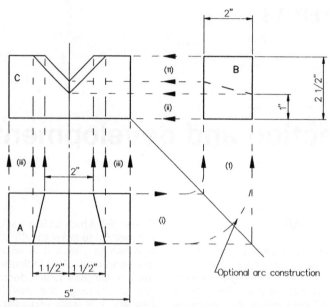

Fig. 13.1 *A first angle projection of a rectangular block incorporating a skew wedge shape. Projection operations are shown in directions (i) (ii) and (iii). Note the minimum dimensions that are necessary. All others are projected.*

Having drawn a projected view, CAD has the added advantage that you can then move the views around to give more or less dimensioning space and you could even swap them about if you wished to change the display between first and third angle projection. There are certainly no feint pencil lines to rub out.

Development of solid shapes

Tubal Cain's book was very full in dealing with the subject of development. That, in general, belongs to a book on drawing technique and not to the present volume. But there are some aspects of development where the CAD process of doing things varies significantly from the manual method, so it is opportune to demonstrate the production of a development from scratch. The best example, and one which covers all the main points, is the development of the frustum of a cone, typical of that shape which is to be found in the cladding of a taper boiler on a steam locomotive.

A significant difference between the two drawing systems is the absence of a pair of dividers in CAD. Now there is, admittedly, a device in the programs for matching the parameters between two items on the screen, which is after all the principal function of the old dividers; but the technique is not as easy to use as the procedure which will now be described. In Fig. 13.2 I have drawn the cone truncated at both ends which will be found in the development section of

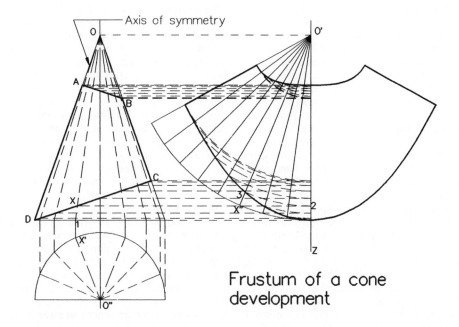

Axis of symmetry

Frustum of a cone
development

Fig. 13.2 *Development of the frustum of a cone. All the construction lines are shown, in this case in broken line format, but on the screen each projection path is in its own unique colour, which makes it easy to project each of the points. All construction lines can be hidden before printing.*

Workshop Drawing by Tubal Cain. The frustum which we want to develop is emboldened as ABCD, the cone being drawn with its centre-line vertical, as usual the centre-lines being on their own layer, distinct from the outline layer. Here is how to proceed.

Draw the elevation of the cone OCD, half cone angle 20° in this case, with its frustum ABCD as the top left view. Next copy the centre-line a convenient distance to the right, O'Z to represent the right-hand side of our projection operations. Now calculate the half angle of the developed shape, in this example 180.sin20, or 61.5636°. The left extremity of the developed view can

now be drawn to this angle from point O' and the eight rays radiating from O' can be generated by means of radial copying the one on the left. In this instance the total angle to span is -61.5636 as above and the total number of items in the array is nine.

Project the plan view below the main elevation: it is only necessary to make a half plan, since the plane of symmetry of the development is formed by the extremities OCD. I chose to divide up the cone into 16 segments, rather than 12 as in the original, since this makes for greater precision. Again, change the layer for the projection lines: they can by this means easily be rubbed out, or

75

better still, hidden when the job is complete. To make things clear I have drawn all the projection lines in broken line format, but this is not strictly essential. Now here is the first valuable departure from manual drawing: instead of having to label the various projection points, simply choose a unique colour on the screen for each of the projection paths. In my example I chose light blue, green, red, yellow, magenta, white, brown and grey for the best contrasting system and as a result there is no problem in following the paths from beginning to end.

You may wish to change the colour of each of the rays in turn on the plan view. You may also wish to change the colour of each of the developed rays to match that of its partner, but I do not find this refinement necessary. With the computer instructed to draw the first colour line, project vertically from the plan to the cone base, X'1 and then join point 1 to the apex O. This will necessitate turning off the orthogonal discipline, a common move during the present procedure. The line O1 intersects the frustum line at X and from this point projects horizontally to the line O'Z at 2. In place of a pair of dividers, strike an arc centre O' and radius O'2, finishing the arc at point 3 on the correct ray from 0'. Repeat this procedure for all eight of the sections and you should find that the arcs end in what will become a smooth curve.

Repeat the procedure for the top part of the frustum; the construction lines are there already and you will save time by projecting the top and bottom views at the same colour setting. The **smooth** lines are now drawn with the CAD version of the French curve, or the Bezier curve, again changing layers to a new one for the finished lines. Give the **Bezier** command and point to each of the arc

ends in turn. As you complete the Bezier curve you may find that the system tries to go haywire and place the final section of the curve in such a way that it does not look like what you want; this is because it sees the last microscopic movement of the mouse and thinks it will follow that for another twist in the curve! You can teach it manners simply by clicking twice on the final point of the arc display; I suppose this is the equivalent of a dressmaker locking the last stitch so that the button does not come off.

You should now have the left halves of the two smooth curves which look correct. Finish the job by performing a mirror image of the array of Bezier curves and outermost ray, reflecting them about the line O'Z. As mentioned earlier, you can now hide all the construction lines on their layers. By these means they could always be regurgitated should that be necessary. Alternatively copy the final shape as a component or save it as a different drawing.

You can now print the shape to full size, as discussed in the section on printing. Remember that if it is too big for the printer or paper to handle in one bite, you can print sections which can then be stuck together with Sellotape. If you need to do this put some reference marks on the drawing at such points that you can pick them up when they are overlaid.

All development shapes work on the same principles and you will normally find that the complete projection process is required to make up for the lack of compasses or dividers. However the ability to repeat a mirror image easily makes the overall process quick and furthermore there is no need to preserve the paper pattern as you would if it had been hand drawn; another copy is easily forthcoming from the printer.

CHAPTER 14

Plotters and printers

If you look in any professional drawing office you will find drawings being run off by plotters. These devices use a number of pens of different colours and produce their prints very quickly and to an excellent standard; they *can* be limited in the styles of text that they can handle and they are designed to take the standard paper sizes, even up to AO size. The maximum paper size dictates the size of the machine bed, its length being great enough to accommodate the smaller of the two dimensions of the largest paper sheet. Of course smaller machines are available.

Plotters have some serious disadvantages:

- They are very expensive.
- They are inflexible, performing no other duty than that of plotting a drawing.
- The pens require maintenance, drying up if they are not stored properly.

The way in which a plotter works is to take each line in turn and then for the paper 'bed' to move under the pen in such a way as to draw the line in its correct location. Thus in drawing a horizontal line the paper moves under the pen without the pen-holder moving, whereas to draw a vertical line the paper stays still and the pen moves over it in its holder. In drawing lines at odd angles and non-linear shapes, both mechanisms move together, a fascinating sight to watch.

I can see no justification at all for having a plotter in the home. A printer does all that is necessary and can be called upon to perform all the other duties involved with a personal computer. It is equally at home printing letters, reports, tables, graphs or drawings and a good printer is capable of working to a very high standard. Instead of treating a drawing as a series of lines and discreet objects, it considers a print as a series of horizontal strips across the page. It works on each strip in turn.

The development of printers over the past 20 years has led to a series of principles on which they work, defined as follows:

- Daisy wheel
- Dot matrix, 8 pin
- Dot matrix, 24 pin
- Inkjet
- Laser

Forget the daisy wheel variety – it can

cope only with text – so we can consider the other four types, any of which will do the job. Going through the series, the price increases and in general so does the quality and speed of operation. Coincidentally the noise produced decreases as we go through the series, although this is not a serious consideration unless there is another nuisance like a television programme going on in the room at the same time as the printer is working.

All CAD programs can cope with the great range of printers which is available on the market and it is vital to 'tell' the system which model you are using. This is all part of the setting up process and quite frankly is easier than the same operation which has to be done when using a word processing program for the first time. The printer is plugged into the back of the computer central processing unit by means of a multi-core cable and it normally goes into No.1 parallel port; don't worry about the jargon, it just means that it is the biggest of the plugs and sockets, so you cannot put it into the wrong hole, nor the wrong way round!

In many computer installations a second port is available, so you can, if you wish, run two devices at will without doing any unplugging. So our choice should be uninhibited by what might be available already.

Let us look at the options in the reverse order of the above list. The laser printer produces the best and most consistent result; it is quick and quiet but is limited normally to one paper size, A4. It is designed expressly for printing office letters and cannot therefore take larger sizes of paper. It is absolutely fine for drawings given the stated limitations, but it should be noted that the laser itself does not have an infinite life and is extremely expensive to replace. Enquire

at your computer store for the new price and that for a new laser unit. Certainly there are such things as wide sheet laser printers, but there again the price goes up by leaps and bounds. Colour laser printers are rare and extremely expensive at present.

Second, the inkjet printer is also designed with office work in mind and is certainly available for sizes A4 and A3. A typical price in late 1998 is £120 for an A4 size and £280 for a comparable A3 model. (Don't take these prices as gospel: I only give them to make a point.) The inkjet unit sprays the paper with myriads of tiny dots, only slightly larger than the laser generated dots and can cope with colour by using a multicolour ink supply cartridge. It is worth going into a store such as *PC World* to see for yourself the impressive demonstration of a colour inkjet printer set up with manufacturers' carefully chosen artwork. The results are most impressive; the image is formed quickly and quietly, but remember that the ink cartridges do not last for ever and are quite expensive to replace, a typical price for a black ink cartridge is £15 to £20 and a colour one much more. Most home office installations in the last few years are kitted out with inkjet printers suitable for A4 size only and one can currently be bought for little over £100, as stated above.

If you mention dot-matrix printers these days many people will turn up their noses and say something about being old-fashioned and having gone out with the ark. Nevertheless they are still made because they can cope with certain applications in a way that no other type can – they physically punch the paper with millions of tiny needle blows so they can print several images deep through carbon or NCR paper. Consequently they are used exclusively for such things as invoice stacks where the customer eventually gets about two dozen copies. You must have had their results when buying things in one of the big stores. The other area where they are still current is in printing wide paper continuous stationery, the typical computer bumph that normally gets consigned straight to the wastepaper basket.

Now you may be beginning to see that by putting together wide paper with continuous feed, we have the recipe for making a print of considerable size using fairly basic equipment. Wide carriage dot-matrix printers are probably the best value you can buy, especially since they are available on the secondhand market, including from computer repair specialists who take them in, clean them up and sell them for significantly less than you would pay for an inkjet A4 printer. As above, the current new price for a wide carriage 24-pin dot-matrix printer is around £130. My own experience is in using a wide carriage 24-pin dot-matrix printer which has actually produced all the artwork for this book, as well as for all the other items which have appeared in the model engineering press over the years. You may care to judge for yourself the quality, for example when it is asked to print a 12 BA screw less than full size. Certainly with the naked eye you cannot see the individual dots and the system makes a good job of such details as fancy fonts with curlicues on all the letters.

Unlike other forms of printer the dot matrix has a ribbon cartridge whose image gradually fades. A replacement costs about £3.00 or £4.00. My own machine also has a colour facility with which it produces a reasonable result in about a half a dozen basic colours, though not to the same standard as the inkjet machines. The colour ribbon is about 1 in. wide and contains four strips of material side by side, black, yellow, red and blue. As with all printers a colour process takes considerably longer than a monochrome one to execute, but that is dealt with later in this chapter.

When the printer types were listed a subdivision was made between an 8- and a 24-pin dot-matrix printer. The smaller number was the original version and it has been supplanted for several years by the 24-pin version. The dots which this produces are so small that they merge together on the page and require a fairly good magnifying glass to see them, while those produced by the old 8-pin version were definitely noticeable. Certainly the dots produced by the 24-pin printer do not present a problem and enable a good range of line widths to be discriminated. Furthermore print quality of the fonts is good, even in small sizes and curves are smooth and free from obvious steps. The computer plots a 'map' of the material to be drawn and gradually produces it as the paper moves in steps beneath the print head. Printing is accompanied by the characteristic buzzing sound as the 24 pins rattle over the page thousands of times a second and the process is relatively slow: as a guide a black and white A4 print takes 5 or 6 minutes to produce, but so what? It has probably taken hours to draw and there is surely a tea break in which to do the printing! A colour print takes about 5 times as long and the larger the paper the longer it takes to get the printed result. I think my record is 2½ hours for a colour print A2 size, but that was after a marathon drawing session.

A2 size did I hear someone say? On a domestic printer? Well almost and with a bit of a fudge, but here is how it is done. A wide carriage printer takes an A3 size sheet of paper laid on its side, 16½ in.

wide. Strictly speaking the print area is only 14 in. wide, so there must be a 1¼ in. margin on the top and bottom of the finished print – not a bad thing anyway. The length of an A2 sheet is approximately 23½ in., so all you have to do is to inform the computer that the page size is 14 in. wide and say 22 in. long and it will happily obey instructions. As stated earlier, the only penalty is the time taken to make a print. As a matter of fact you can specify an even longer length of print if you wish to print on a 'toilet roll', provided that you can get hold of a long enough piece of paper.

So those are the choices before you in the printing line. Whatever you choose you will be amazed at the quality produced, so we can now explore the exciting possibilities that are available with this new technology. Unlike the old drawing-board system you are not lumbered with the rigid artwork that you have drawn, either in quality or size (or scale) and the possibilities are as wide as you can imagine. The first step is to make sure that your computer understands what model of printer it is dealing with. This is covered in the installation procedure of the program, which should include recognition of all the common models of printers and plotters. These are listed and it is just a matter of identifying the correct model in the list. One word of advice if you are limited for disc space: you don't have to install *all* the makes of machine which are in the program supplied, although the easy way to do the installation is to accept a full package.

You may still have the choice between a colour or black and white printer. Unless you are actually wanting to print in colour, inform the machine that it is a black and white model, since that considerably speeds up the printing process.

Should you fit a black ribbon in a colour machine, it will still work although if the program thinks it is dealing with a colour machine it will ration out the memory in a different way and slow down the printing process.

Line widths

As already mentioned elsewhere, enhanced line widths get in the way of clear screen presentation and everything should be drawn at minimum line width for clarity. Changing the width before printing is easy provided that you have kept to the rules about layers: it is simple to operate on one layer at a time. You will find that the computer offers a choice of line width and probably gives what looks like some broad brush strokes at the thick end of the spectrum. Test these out on your printer and form a view of the parts of the range which are appropriate for your own needs. It is probable that different printing systems will respond differently to the commands for line width and it is not possible to lay down hard and fast rules. As an example, however, I use line thickness 0 for all dimension lines, centre-lines and hatchings and go up 3 graduations for the main lines within a drawing. If I need to emphasise a line such as that forming say an alteration or even the dark side of a 'shadow line', then I go up another 3 graduations. I find that the intermediate values do not have the significance required, but do not take this exposition as gospel without trying it out for yourself. I rather suspect that the fine range of graduations offered in the program menu stem from the normal industrial practice of using a plotter which may respond rather more sensitively to the line width command than is the case with a dot-matrix printer. Furthermore a laser printer starts with the ability to produce a slightly finer line at the narrow end of the spectrum, so it is logical that it can draw thicker lines with rather more width steps than a dot-matrix machine can. But don't let that put you off from the cheaper printer options; judge for yourself from the reproductions in this book for a start.

Line width commands have a varying response from different fonts. For example, the widely used varieties such as **Roman-S** are sensitive to the width command because they are formed of two parallel sets of lines which are each broadened by the width command; but the solid fonts such as Helvetica and Times Roman are rigidly formed and do not respond to variation in line thickness. They do get bolder as their sizes are increased.

Line multipliers

Here we are delving into the more arcane features of the program system. You lay down lines on the screen that look right: centre-lines have their dashes and dots correctly spaced out and broken lines fill their allocated spaces in a way that looks correct. You will notice that as you zoom out to include a large drawing on the screen, so the discontinuous lines tend to merge, but you know that they are still correctly designated and whenever you zoom in on a small part of the screen the expected details appear again. The subdivisions of line types enable the lengths of the dashes to be varied according to the type and size of drawing and you will assemble on the screen a format that looks correct before printing.

Now when you print a drawing it is necessary to inform the computer what scale it is working in. This enables it to adjust the scale of the discontinuous

lines to show up properly. In other words, the objective is to get a given format of discontinuous line to look on paper as it did on the screen, so this is where the line size multiplier comes in. Certainly in my own program there is no hard and fast direction given to enable an intelligent guess to be made as to the correct value for any particular degree of reduction, or zoom – we are in the realms of trial and error. It may not be as simple as matching the line size multiplier with the zoom figure; for example for the best results I have discovered that a value of 0.07 fits when printing full size or even at half size, but when printing $\frac{1}{70}$ full size (ie a zoom value of 70) a line multiplier value of 10 works best. I suspect this may not be the same for all programs, or more particularly for all printers. The worst problems seem to arise when printing in colour, when the horizontal lines may be correctly broken, but the vertical ones print continuous. You should realise that the line size multiplier command affects the whole drawing, so you must experiment with several tests of printing to get the best results. Some examples are given in Fig. 14.1 which has been assembled from several different drawings overprinted on the same page.

Selective printing

You should find that the machine prepares to print the whole of the drawing you have produced to fill the whole of the page whose size you have defined. That may or may not be what you want it to do. You will find the facility for choosing a given magnification (or reduction) to suit your purpose. For example, some of the drawings in this book have been printed full size, while others have been reduced by 50% or

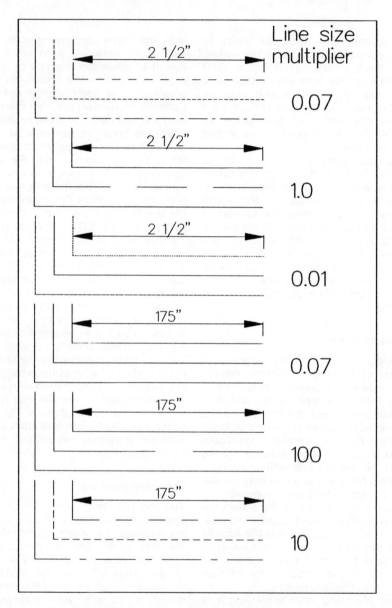

Fig. 14.1 *Tests of lines at different line size multipliers. The top three views are printed full size, the line size multipliers being 0.07 (my best figure), 1.0 and 0.01. You will see how the line breaks disappear in the second and third prints. For the second trio of views the lines are magnified to 70 times their original size, as witnessed by the dimension lines. The original 0.07 figure just produces continuous print, while 100 seems to have gone too far. The best compromise is at a value of 10.*

even further. In computer parlance they may talk about a zoom factor −2 representing a drawing at a scale of half full size; an alternative notation is to give a percentage reduction, but you should soon get to understand the instruction on the screen.

Another useful facility is to be able to select a specific part of a drawing to print. This is done in a similar way to one of the editing commands, namely by means of windows, crossings etc., drawn on the drawing, thus you can keep a large drawing intact and tell the machine to pick out a small detail for manufacture. I normally use this technique to produce decent size prints for the workshop. Where possible full size is the most useful, although I try to resist scaling a drawing if at all possible! From the above you will deduce advantages not present in the old drawing office regime, namely that of deciding on drawing size at the printing stage and of carving up sections of a drawing without using scissors. Normally my workshop contains current drawings for production purposes on A4 sheets, with an occasional A3 copy where necessary. On the work which I do there is little cause to resort to A2 size, but a large boiler is an exception, which illustrates the point made in the discussion of printer types. Drawings once used are usually recycled for scrap paper in the workshop and there is no bar on doodling on them, since other copies are easily available.

Unconventional applications

Let us now explore some of the possibilities which CAD printing can produce to advantage. At art shops sticky paper is available that has its glue dispersed as tiny bubbles (called vesicular adhesive). The glue is very strong and needs very little wetting, so that the dimensions of the paper do not change. The first example of its use is in the repair of the escapement of a long-case clock, an example of which is often in my workshop. Over the years the escape wheel wears a groove in the anchor pallets and many have been repaired by soldering little pieces of spring steel to the pallet faces to give the clock several years' more life. It is, however, very rewarding to make a whole new anchor assembly out of gauge plate which is then hardened and tempered and should provide a very long life indeed. The geometry of clock pallets is well documented and lends itself to a CAD drawing to get the right profile to a greater accuracy than our forefathers would have produced. Fig. 14.2 is a drawing of an anchor from one of the clocks that has come through

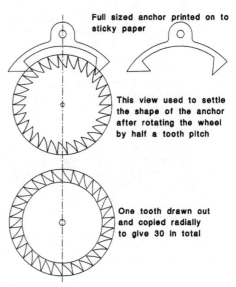

Full sized anchor printed on to sticky paper

This view used to settle the shape of the anchor after rotating the wheel by half a tooth pitch

One tooth drawn out and copied radially to give 30 in total

Fig. 14.2 *An escapement anchor for a long-case clock drawn out and printed full size on sticky paper for cutting out of gauge-plate.*

my workshop in a sorry state. A print is made on the sticky paper *exactly* full size and the paper is stuck on to a clean piece of gauge plate. I then use a Hegner saw to cut around the pattern with very little still to be removed by filing. Using the thinnest print line possible, the accuracy is better than can be produced by drawing with a scriber and dividers on well blued gauge plate and it is surprising how the sticky paper adheres to the metal during the sawing process.

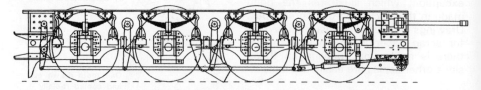

Fig. 14.3 *A nameplate template for printing 8 in. long onto sticky paper which is then applied to brass sheet before being cut out and sweated to the backing plate.*

The second example is of a nameplate for a 7¼ in. narrow gauge locomotive (see Fig. 14.3). One option was obviously to make a pattern and to get two castings made, but fabrication was straightforward from sheet brass. The first problem was how to decide the correct form of letters and their spacing. I chose **Helvetica** upper case letters and altered their aspect ratio by trial and error until they 'looked right'. The computer did the rest to determine the exact shape and spacing and all that was left to judgement was the border. Several attempts were made at printing in different sizes, before deciding on the right looking one. At the chosen magnification a print was made on sticky paper which was then applied to a sheet of 16 gauge brass. Cutting around the letters was done to an accuracy of about 0.005 in. (with the aid of a good magnifier) and the loose letters and edge strips were cleaned up with needle files. The backing sheet was marked with the letter spacing from a spare print and the letters were sweated on with soft solder. The result is very gratifying. I certainly do not have the knowledge of the sign writer's trade to enable me to produce good-looking letters by the conventional route.

So you will see that with a little imagination, the world is your oyster: CAD printing has all these advantages of flexibility in terms of size, selectivity, consistency and above all, accuracy. Just look at the detail even in small size in the greatly reduced copy Fig. 14.4.

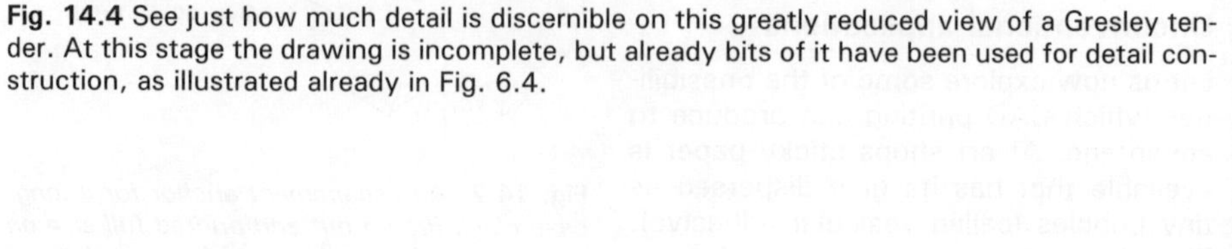

Fig. 14.4 See just how much detail is discernible on this greatly reduced view of a Gresley tender. At this stage the drawing is incomplete, but already bits of it have been used for detail construction, as illustrated already in Fig. 6.4.

CHAPTER 15

File management

Each time you make a drawing you create what the computer calls a file. Very quickly you should discover the way the program saves such a file. Do not wait until the end of a session: it is possible to lose all the work you have done should there be some sort of a problem; it is possible to hit the wrong button in some circumstances and remember you are always vulnerable to a powercut, especially in rural areas in stormy weather conditions. It may be possible inadvertently to try to get the computer to do something it does not want to do and in such circumstances all normal response to the keys or mouse movements may fail; if the file has not been saved the recent work may be lost if and when you have to make an emergency escape from the program. Do get into the habit of saving your work every few minutes, or every time you have completed a phase of modification.

Now how do you go about saving a drawing? The instructions are quite specific in all the programs that I have seen, but you will have to choose a file name and this is where your ingenuity comes into its own. You have up to eight letters (and/or numbers) with which to invent a new name, so work out a plan of campaign which is easy for you to understand. I try to have a number of series of names; thus, for example, if I am doing a job for someone else (like the clock escapement in Fig. 14.2) the file will carry that person's name, or an abbreviation of it. On the other hand major projects will be reminiscent of the job drawn, eg the tender drawing in Fig. 14.4 is called 'Tendera4' and subdivisions of it that are filed separately start off with 'Tend....' and have a suffix which I can recognise! It does not take all that long to amass 100 files, so if you do not make a system you will get into a mess. I suppose you could keep a drawing register like they do in large companies, but there does not seem any point to me in having an elaborate numbering system just for your own use. The way most programs store the files, you will be presented with a list of all the files in the system when you load the one you want. Invariably the display is in alphabetical order, or more precisely alphanumeric order; thus Plonk10 comes before Plonk2, if you see what I mean! The way around this problem in a series with letters and numbers is to use a 0 prefix. So Plonk 2 would become Plonk02, thereby taking its natural turn in the queue, well before Plonk10.

In all programs there will be a suffix added, such as .DXF and this suffix merely denotes that the file is a drawing. If you are handling the files you have produced you can normally ignore this suffix in everyday use. You will also find a facility for creating a back-up file and this should certainly be done for any work which is the product of several hours' labour. It would be very frustrating to lose a drawing beyond recall and there are several causes of failure in which a file can become damaged: computers are not infallible and you can suffer some sort of mechanical or electronic damage which may affect the work you have done. On one occasion I had the misfortune to suffer a hard disc failure which effectively disabled the machine. In the event I was able to recover all my files, but there were some anxious moments!

Consider making copies of all your files every few weeks onto floppy discs; these are very cheap and each disc will hold an enormous amount of information. As a guide, the whole of my tender drawing occupies only about 17% of a single disc capacity, including all the details as shown in several figures in this book. I make a copy every few weeks and get my next door neighbour to hold the discs, so that they are not vulnerable to fire or theft from the area of production.

Another thing which you should consider is purging your computer disc of all the old files with which you have finished. Having copied them onto a floppy disc you can erase the files from the computer memory and this will not only free up useful space but also reduce the list down which you have to look when you want to reload a file. After such a clean-up operation it is very simple to retrieve any of these files from the floppy disc should that be required. The universal convention is that your floppy disc drive is called 'A', so when you are asked to choose which file you wish to load you simply type in A:\ followed by the name of the file, not forgetting this time the suffix which it contains. There may be reasons why you do not wish to lose the old files from the computer store itself. In these circumstances consider moving the old ones to a new directory in such a way that you can gain access to it easily.

Other systems

This book is not dealing with computer-aided machining (CAM) but your drawings will be suitable for feeding into a machine which is computer controlled. The universal format is that laid down in *Autocad*, so you must translate the file into a .DXF form, an operation which you can easily perform within any of the programs. Again the finished file should be stored on a floppy disc. By these means it is also possible to send your files to other users and the .DXF format is the common denominator. The obvious application for computer-generated drawings in the model engineering world is laser cutting: any company which offers a laser cutting service requires only the .DXF file of your drawing, from which they will enter the offset of the laser cut thickness to produce the superb results which have gained popularity in recent years. Should you import somebody else's files in another system and make use of the converse process, you may well find that there are some features of the files which need cleaning up. One obvious source of problem is the font library in which you may find that the originating machine has different styles from the receiving machine. In these cases a small amount of work may be necessary.

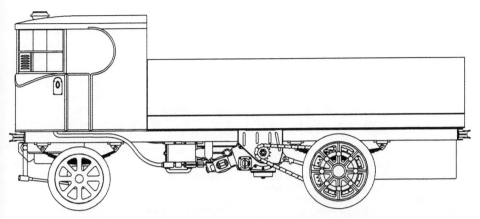

Fig. 15.1 *This view of a sentinel waggon is reproduced to ¹/₅₀ full size; nevertheless much detail is discernible. The drawing was done originally on* Autocad *and transferred to my computer as a .DXF file on a floppy disc with no problem at all. (Drawing done originally by Norman Smedley whose cooperation and consent to publish are acknowledged.)*

Take Fig. 15.1 as an example: this drawing was originally done in *Autocad* and entered on to my system from a floppy disc. It goes without saying that some of the settings which were included in the original were not the same as I normally use, but these are easy to correct. One example of this divergence is the layer system imported from *Autocad*; the tagging of some of the original layers was by means of names, others by the word 'layer' followed by a number. Although this designation is quite foreign to my program, the differently named layers appeared on my display when I called up a layer change. There is no problem with renaming the layers in any way you wish and this drawing poses no problem now it is in my system.

Other sides to the program

What you have bought does not confine you to the things described in this book:

in the component library which comes with the program you will discover many of the symbols required for architectural drawings and those for the other branches of engineering. Lest you should think of me as typecast in a mechanical mould, see Fig. 15.2 which illustrates an application of some of the electrical data available. The more you experiment the more you will discover of the latent ability which lies untapped. In my own case I always try to do a drawing first, especially when somebody else is involved. I well remember a friend who now lives in Galloway asking me if I could make a glass fire surround for him, edged with brass channel. He is not an engineer and our mutual understanding of things brass and glass was less than perfect. When he paid me a visit I had done a drawing of what I thought he wanted, only to find that I had drawn it upside-down for his requirements! Use of the **whoops** button is much simpler and cheaper than cutting metal. In another anecdote, my daughter

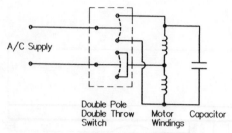

A/C Supply

Double Pole
Double Throw   Motor   Capacitor
Switch   Windings

Fig. 15.2 *A simple electrical drawing for the wiring of a motor. The components are selected from the component library already available within the programme. The amount of material within the component library is quite formidable although most of it will be found to be absolutely useless. In most circumstances it is probably better to create one's own components that are exactly what is required.*

who lives in the Netherlands wanted some curtains made here for her tall Dutch windows. A drawing of *exactly* what the carpenter could do with the curtain track sorted out any problem before valuable curtain material was cut up.

Parts lists

All programs have the facility for assembling a parts list, or 'bill of materials'. I find this side of the process particularly cumbersome and cannot get my own program to produce it in the way I would value. Try yours when you are ready, but I do not think that this facility has any real value in model engineering.

Measurement

At any time you can interrogate a drawing to find an exact dimension and provided that you have obeyed the ground rules you should find this facility

most useful. Measurements available include lengths and angles and of course lengths of such things as circles. You should also find a display of the status of items in a drawing and your program keeps track of all the items you have drawn, so that if you even want to know how many circles there are, it can tell you. The other important 'utility' department is that which controls file saving, storage and copying. You must get to understand how it works and become proficient in its operation.

Improving your technique

The more you get into CAD the more you will learn about the system and what it can and cannot do easily. This book has attempted to point you in the direction of exploration of the various methods available. You may never use all the many facilities but you will certainly master the important ones quite quickly. Looking back on my own experience I remember the first fortnight being hell and producing one drawing in that time. While I got the basic thing right by trial and error and frequent use of the **whoops** button, the end result was not perfect. Little things eluded me such as the correct range of line widths to use, while printer compatibility in the finest sense came only by fine tuning; it was some time before I latched on to the full range of fonts available and the easy way to change things which were not quite right without a total redraw.

The best advice I can offer is as follows:

- Become au fait with all that is taught in the tutorial of your program – that should take days rather than weeks.
- Start with a fairly simple drawing and practise all the relevant movements which have been described.

88

- Work out your own strategy for dealing with layers and colours. As already mentioned it does make sense to keep all centre-lines on their own layer, similarly dimensions, hatchings and text. You should not hesitate to split the layers for the principal drawing lines, since it is always easier to combine them rather than to split them.
- Use the thinnest line width for all the drawing work, only enhancing the width of the relevant lines before putting the drawing to bed and printing it. In this regard you may find a **quick draw** facility within your program which displays all lines as minimum thickness, but also disguises their nature until the normal format is restored. This procedure is only recommended as a means of examining details on a drawing which has already been completed.
- Sell your drawing board while the going is good! It took me just over a year to take this step and I found a willing purchaser at a reasonable price in one of our local town's shops. The disposal of the board revealed a corner of the office which I had forgotten about for several years! This in turn allows further storage space for engineering materials which seems far more productive than the former way of doing things.